Learn

Eureka Math®
Grade 1
Modules 4 & 5

Published by Great Minds®.

Copyright © 2018 Great Minds®.

Printed in the U.S.A.
This book may be purchased from the publisher at eureka-math.org.
7 8 9 10 CCR 24 23 22

ISBN 978-1-64054-052-1

G1-M4-M5-L-05.2018

Learn ◆ Practice ◆ Succeed

Eureka Math® student materials for *A Story of Units*® (K–5) are available in the *Learn, Practice, Succeed* trio. This series supports differentiation and remediation while keeping student materials organized and accessible. Educators will find that the *Learn, Practice,* and *Succeed* series also offers coherent—and therefore, more effective—resources for Response to Intervention (RTI), extra practice, and summer learning.

Learn

Eureka Math Learn serves as a student's in-class companion where they show their thinking, share what they know, and watch their knowledge build every day. *Learn* assembles the daily classwork—Application Problems, Exit Tickets, Problem Sets, templates—in an easily stored and navigated volume.

Practice

Each *Eureka Math* lesson begins with a series of energetic, joyous fluency activities, including those found in *Eureka Math Practice.* Students who are fluent in their math facts can master more material more deeply. With *Practice,* students build competence in newly acquired skills and reinforce previous learning in preparation for the next lesson.

Together, *Learn* and *Practice* provide all the print materials students will use for their core math instruction.

Succeed

Eureka Math Succeed enables students to work individually toward mastery. These additional problem sets align lesson by lesson with classroom instruction, making them ideal for use as homework or extra practice. Each problem set is accompanied by a Homework Helper, a set of worked examples that illustrate how to solve similar problems.

Teachers and tutors can use *Succeed* books from prior grade levels as curriculum-consistent tools for filling gaps in foundational knowledge. Students will thrive and progress more quickly as familiar models facilitate connections to their current grade-level content.

Students, families, and educators:

Thank you for being part of the *Eureka Math*® community, where we celebrate the joy, wonder, and thrill of mathematics.

In the *Eureka Math* classroom, new learning is activated through rich experiences and dialogue. The *Learn* book puts in each student's hands the prompts and problem sequences they need to express and consolidate their learning in class.

What is in the Learn book?

Application Problems: Problem solving in a real-world context is a daily part of *Eureka Math*. Students build confidence and perseverance as they apply their knowledge in new and varied situations. The curriculum encourages students to use the RDW process—Read the problem, Draw to make sense of the problem, and Write an equation and a solution. Teachers facilitate as students share their work and explain their solution strategies to one another.

Problem Sets: A carefully sequenced Problem Set provides an in-class opportunity for independent work, with multiple entry points for differentiation. Teachers can use the Preparation and Customization process to select "Must Do" problems for each student. Some students will complete more problems than others; what is important is that all students have a 10-minute period to immediately exercise what they've learned, with light support from their teacher.

Students bring the Problem Set with them to the culminating point of each lesson: the Student Debrief. Here, students reflect with their peers and their teacher, articulating and consolidating what they wondered, noticed, and learned that day.

Exit Tickets: Students show their teacher what they know through their work on the daily Exit Ticket. This check for understanding provides the teacher with valuable real-time evidence of the efficacy of that day's instruction, giving critical insight into where to focus next.

Templates: From time to time, the Application Problem, Problem Set, or other classroom activity requires that students have their own copy of a picture, reusable model, or data set. Each of these templates is provided with the first lesson that requires it.

Where can I learn more about Eureka Math *resources?*

The Great Minds® team is committed to supporting students, families, and educators with an ever-growing library of resources, available at eureka-math.org. The website also offers inspiring stories of success in the *Eureka Math* community. Share your insights and accomplishments with fellow users by becoming a *Eureka Math* Champion.

Best wishes for a year filled with aha moments!

Jill Diniz

Jill Diniz
Director of Mathematics
Great Minds

The Read–Draw–Write Process

The *Eureka Math* curriculum supports students as they problem-solve by using a simple, repeatable process introduced by the teacher. The Read–Draw–Write (RDW) process calls for students to

1. Read the problem.
2. Draw and label.
3. Write an equation.
4. Write a word sentence (statement).

Educators are encouraged to scaffold the process by interjecting questions such as

- What do you see?
- Can you draw something?
- What conclusions can you make from your drawing?

The more students participate in reasoning through problems with this systematic, open approach, the more they internalize the thought process and apply it instinctively for years to come.

Contents

Module 4: Place Value, Comparison, Addition and Subtraction to 40

Module 5: Identifying, Composing, and Partitioning Shapes

Grade 1
Module 4

Read

Joy is holding 10 marbles in 1 hand and 10 marbles in the other hand. How many marbles does she have in all?

Draw

Write

_____

_____

_____

Name _____ Date _____

Circle groups of 10. Write the number to show the total amount of objects.

1. There are _____ grapes.	2. There are _____ carrots.
3. There are _____ apples.	4. There are _____ peanuts.
5. There are _____ grapes.	6. There are _____ carrots.
7. There are _____ apples.	8. There are _____ peanuts.

EUREKA MATH

Lesson 1: Compare the efficiency of counting by ones and counting by tens.

5

© 2018 Great Minds®. eureka-math.org

Make a number bond to show tens and ones.

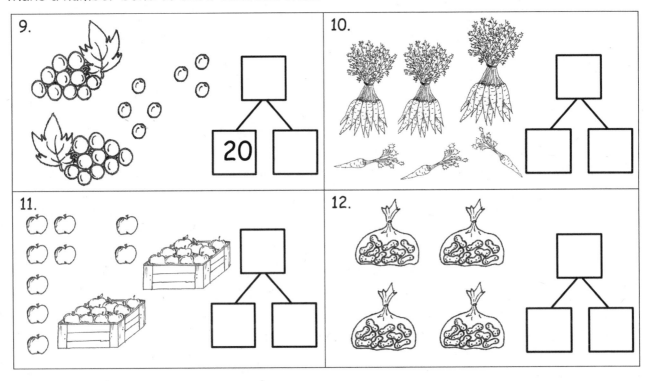

Make a number bond to show tens and ones. Circle tens to help.

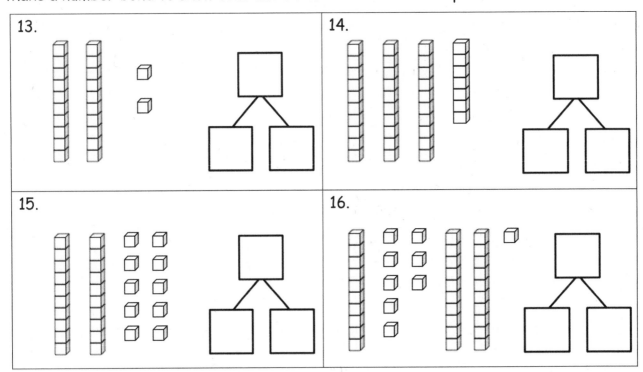

Lesson 1:   Compare the efficiency of counting by ones and counting by tens.

EUREKA
MATH®

Name _____   Date _____

Complete the number bonds.

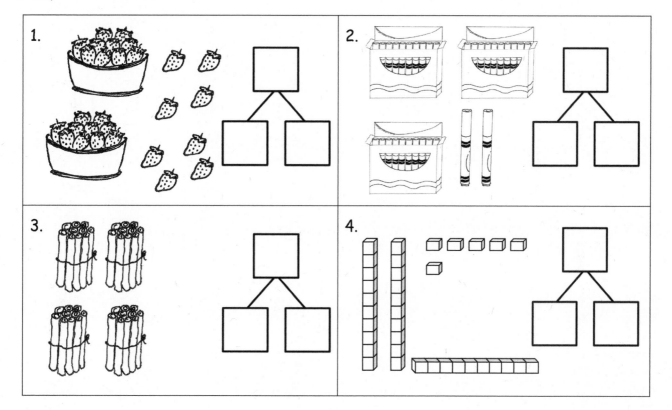

Read

Ted has 4 boxes with 10 pencils in each box. How many pencils does he have altogether?

Draw

Write

_____

_____

_____

Lesson 2:   Use the place value chart to record and name tens and ones within a two-digit number.

© 2018 Great Minds®. eureka-math.org

9

Name _____   Date _____

Write the tens and ones and say the numbers. Complete the statement.

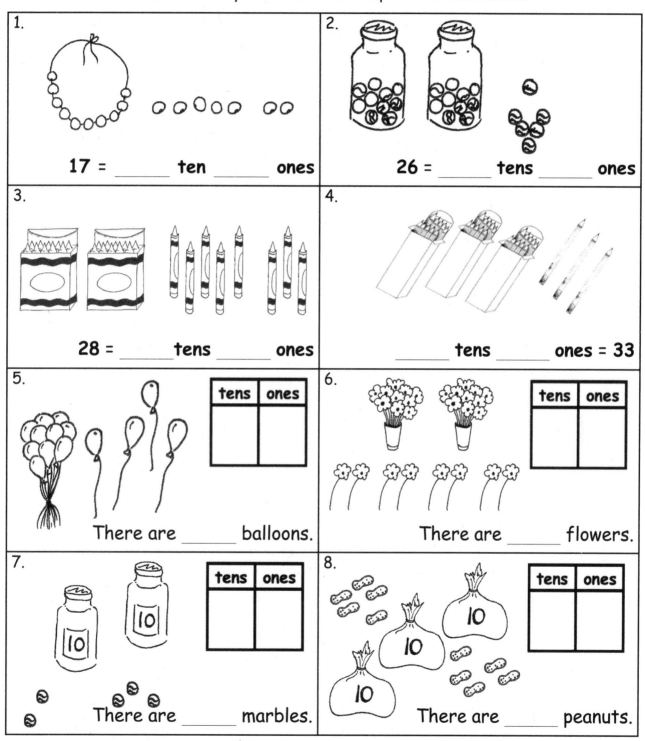

1.

17 = _____ ten _____ ones

2.

26 = _____ tens _____ ones

3.

28 = _____ tens _____ ones

4.

_____ tens _____ ones = 33

5.

tens	ones

There are _____ balloons.

6.

tens	ones

There are _____ flowers.

7.

tens	ones

There are _____ marbles.

8.

tens	ones

There are _____ peanuts.

EUREKA
MATH

Lesson 2:   Use the place value chart to record and name tens and ones within a
two-digit number.

© 2018 Great Minds®. eureka-math.org

11

Write the tens and ones. Complete the statement.

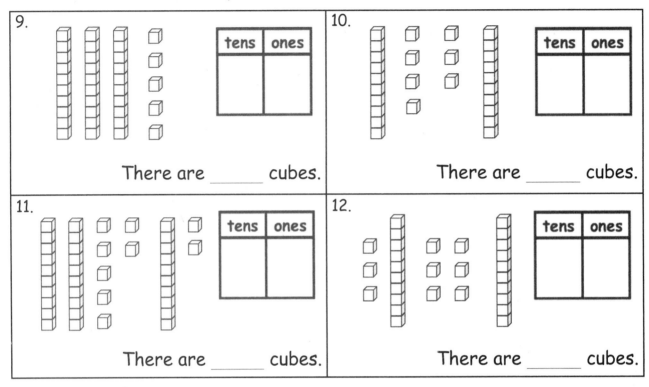

9.

tens	ones

There are _____ cubes.

10.

tens	ones

There are _____ cubes.

11.

tens	ones

There are _____ cubes.

12.

tens	ones

There are _____ cubes.

Write the missing numbers. Say them the regular way and the Say Ten way.

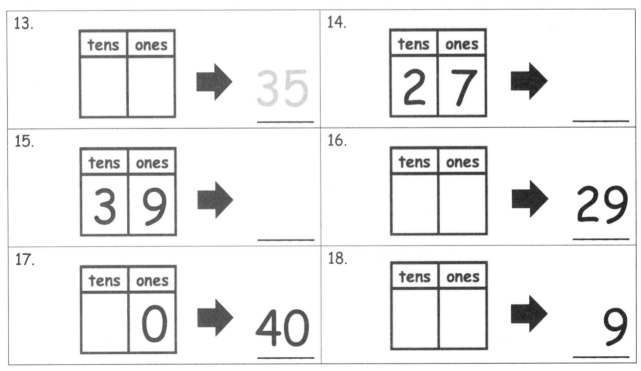

13.

tens	ones

➡ 35
___

14.

tens	ones
2	7

➡
___

15.

tens	ones
3	9

➡
___

16.

tens	ones

➡ 29
___

17.

tens	ones
	0

➡ 40
___

18.

tens	ones

➡ 9
___

Lesson 2:   Use the place value chart to record and name tens and ones within a
             two-digit number.

EUREKA
MATH

Name _____   Date _____

Match the picture to the place value chart that shows the correct tens and ones.

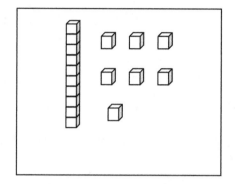

tens	ones
4	0

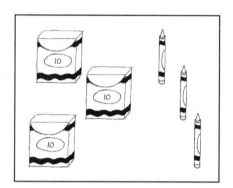

tens	ones
1	7

tens	ones
3	3

EUREKA MATH

Lesson 2:   Use the place value chart to record and name tens and ones within a two-digit number.

13

© 2018 Great Minds®. eureka-math.org

tens	ones

place value chart

Read

Sue is writing the number 34 on a place value chart. She cannot remember if she has 4 tens and 3 ones or 3 tens and 4 ones.

Use a place value chart to show how many tens and ones are in 34.

Use a drawing and words to explain this to Sue.

Draw

Lesson 3:   Interpret two-digit numbers as either tens and some ones or as all ones.

© 2018 Great Minds®. eureka-math.org

17

Write

Lesson 3:   Interpret two-digit numbers as either tens and some ones or as all ones.

© 2018 Great Minds®. eureka-math.org

EUREKA
MATH®

Name _____   Date _____

Count as many tens as you can. Complete each statement. Say the numbers and the sentences.

1.	2.
_____ ten _____ ones is the same as _____ ones.	_____ tens _____ ones is the same as _____ ones.
3.	4.
_____ tens _____ ones is the same as _____ ones.	_____ tens _____ ones is the same as _____ ones.
5.	6.
_____ tens _____ ones is the same as _____ ones.	_____ tens _____ ones is the same as _____ ones.

Lesson 3:   Interpret two-digit numbers as either tens and some ones or as all ones.

© 2018 Great Minds®. eureka-math.org

Match.

7. | 3 tens 2 ones |

    | 29 ones |

8.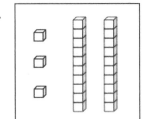

    | 40 ones |

    | 23 ones |

9. | 37 ones |

    | 32 ones |

10. | 4 tens |

    | 17 ones |

11.

    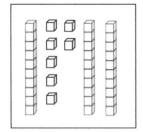

12. | 9 ones 2 tens |

Fill in the missing numbers.

13. **15** ➡ 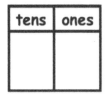 ➡ _____ ones

14. _____ ➡ _____ tens _____ ones ➡ 39 ones

Lesson 3:   Interpret two-digit numbers as either tens and some ones or as all
ones.

EUREKA
MATH

Name _____   Date _____

Count as many tens as you can. Complete each statement. Say the numbers and the sentences.

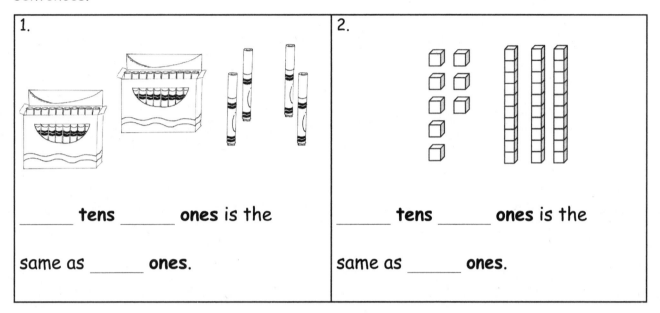

1.

_____ **tens** _____ **ones** is the

same as _____ **ones**.

2.

_____ **tens** _____ **ones** is the

same as _____ **ones**.

Fill in the missing numbers.

3. **27**   ➡

tens	ones

   ➡   _____ **ones**

EUREKA MATH®

Lesson 3:   Interpret two-digit numbers as either tens and some ones or as all ones.

© 2018 Great Minds®. eureka-math.org

21

Read

Lisa has 3 boxes of 10 crayons, as well as 5 extra crayons. Sally has 19 crayons. Sally says she has more crayons, but Lisa disagrees. Who is right?

Draw

 Lesson 4: Write and interpret two-digit numbers as addition sentences that combine tens and ones.

© 2018 Great Minds®. eureka-math.org

23

Write

_____

_____

_____

Lesson 4:   Write and interpret two-digit numbers as addition sentences that combine tens and ones.

Name _____   Date _____

Fill in the number bond. Complete the sentences.

1.

| 20 |
| 3 |

20 and 3 make _____.

20 + 3 = _____

2.

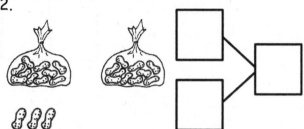

20 and 8 make _____.

20 + 8 = _____

3.

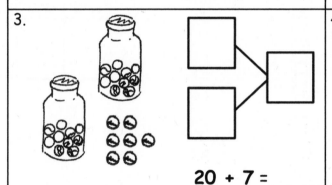

20 + 7 = _____

7 more than 20 is _____.

4.

6 more than 30 is _____.

30 + 6 = _____

5.

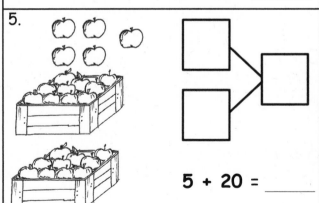

5 + 20 = _____

20 more than 5 is _____.

6.

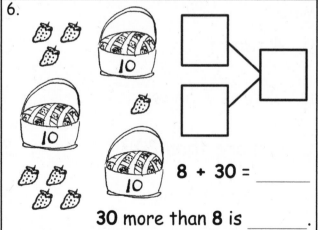 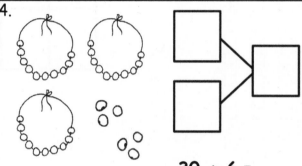

8 + 30 = _____

30 more than 8 is _____.

EUREKA
MATH®

Lesson 4:   Write and interpret two-digit numbers as addition sentences that
combine tens and ones.

25

© 2018 Great Minds®. eureka-math.org

Write the tens and ones. Then, write an addition sentence to add the tens and ones.

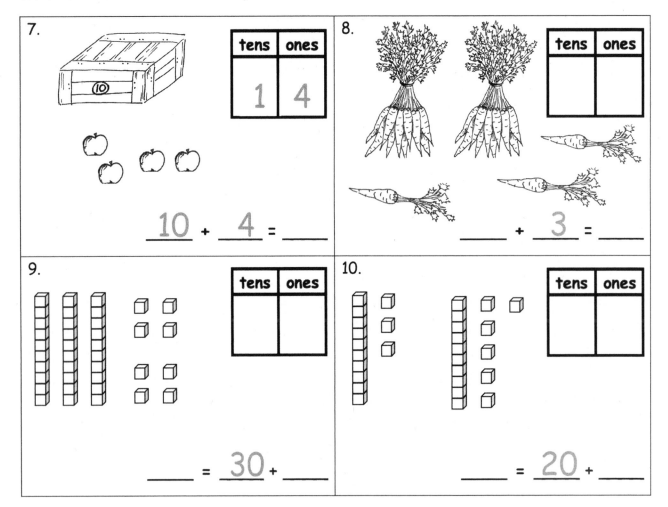

7.

tens	ones
1	4

___10___ + ___4___ = _____

8.

tens	ones

_____ + ___3___ = _____

9.

tens	ones

_____ = ___30___ + _____

10.

tens	ones

_____ = ___20___ + _____

Match.

11. 4 tens •   • 20 + 7

12. 2 tens 7 ones •   • 40

13. 3 more than 20 •   • 20 + 3

14. 9 ones 3 tens •   • 2 + 30

15. 2 ones 3 tens •   • 9 + 30

Lesson 4:   Write and interpret two-digit numbers as addition sentences that
                    combine tens and ones.

EUREKA
MATH

Name _____   Date _____

Write the tens and ones. Then, write an addition sentence to add the tens and ones.

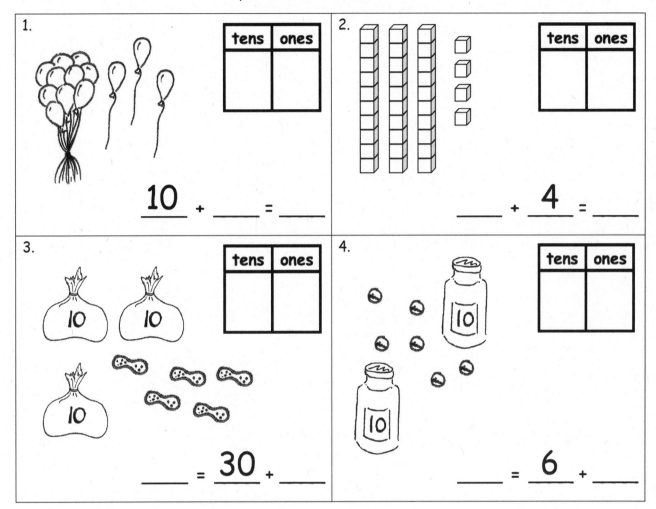

1.

tens	ones

_10_ + ____ = ____

2.

tens	ones

____ + _4_ = ____

3.

tens	ones

____ = _30_ + ____

4.

tens	ones

____ = _6_ + ____

Lesson 4:   Write and interpret two-digit numbers as addition sentences that combine tens and ones.

27

EUREKA MATH®

Read

Lee has 4 pencils and buys 10 more. Kiana has 17 pencils and loses 10 of them. Who has more pencils now? Use drawings, words, and number sentences to explain your thinking.

Draw

Lesson 5:   Identify 10 more, 10 less, 1 more, and 1 less then a two-digit number.

29

© 2018 Great Minds®. eureka-math.org

Write

_____

_____

_____

Lesson 5:   Identify 10 more, 10 less, 1 more, and 1 less then a two-digit number.

EUREKA MATH

Name _____   Date _____

Write the number.

1.

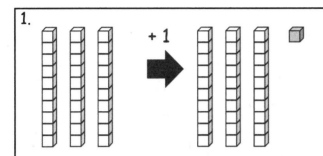

1 more than 30 is _____.

2.

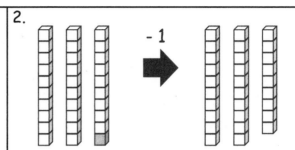

1 less than 30 is _____.

3.

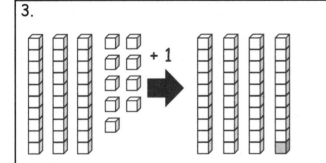

1 more than 39 is _____.

4.

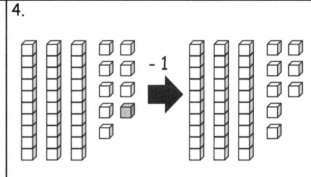

1 less than 39 is _____.

5.

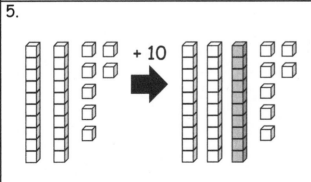

10 more than 27 is _____.

6.

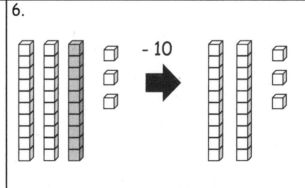

10 less than 33 is _____.

Draw 1 more or 10 more. You may use a quick ten to show 10 more.

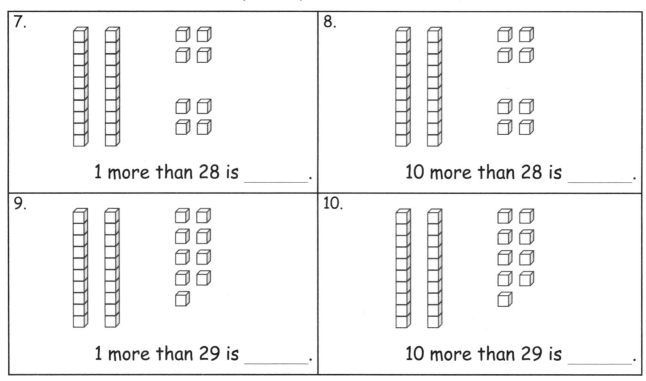

7.
1 more than 28 is _____.

8.
10 more than 28 is _____.

9.
1 more than 29 is _____.

10.
10 more than 29 is _____.

Cross off (x) to show 1 less or 10 less.

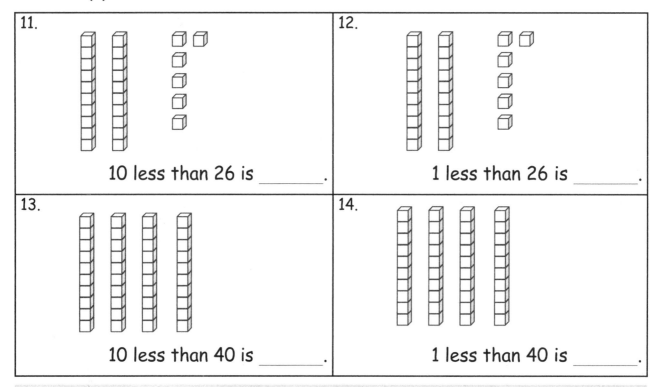

11.
10 less than 26 is _____.

12.
1 less than 26 is _____.

13.
10 less than 40 is _____.

14.
1 less than 40 is _____.

Lesson 5:   Identify 10 more, 10 less, 1 more, and 1 less then a two-digit number.

Name _____   Date _____

Draw 1 more or 10 more. You may use a quick ten to show 10 more.

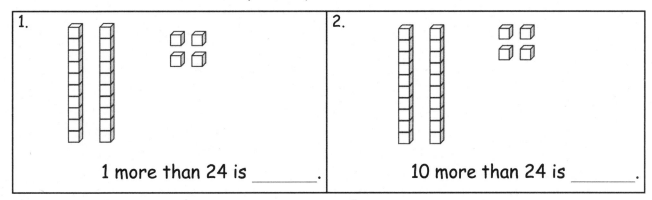

1. 1 more than 24 is _____.

2. 10 more than 24 is _____.

Cross off (x) to show 1 less or 10 less.

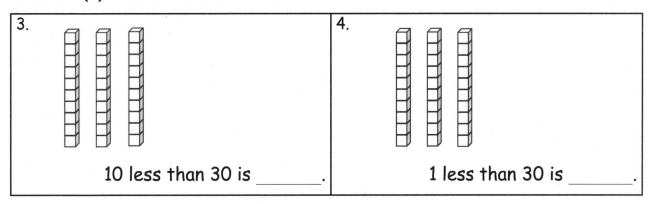

3. 10 less than 30 is _____.

4. 1 less than 30 is _____.

EUREKA MATH

Lesson 5:   Identify 10 more, 10 less, 1 more, and 1 less then a two-digit number.

33

© 2018 Great Minds®. eureka-math.org

tens	ones

tens	ones

double place value charts

© 2018 Great Minds®. eureka-math.org

Read

Sheila has 3 bags with 10 pretzels in each bag and 9 extra pretzels. She gives 1 bag to a friend. How many pretzels does she have now?

Extension: John has 19 pretzels. How many more pretzels does he need to have as many as Sheila has now?

Draw

Lesson 6:   Use dimes and pennies as representations of tens and ones.

© 2018 Great Minds®. eureka-math.org

37

Write

_____

_____

_____

    Lesson 6:   Use dimes and pennies as representations of tens and ones.

EUREKA
MATH

Name _____   Date _____

Fill in the place value chart and the blanks.

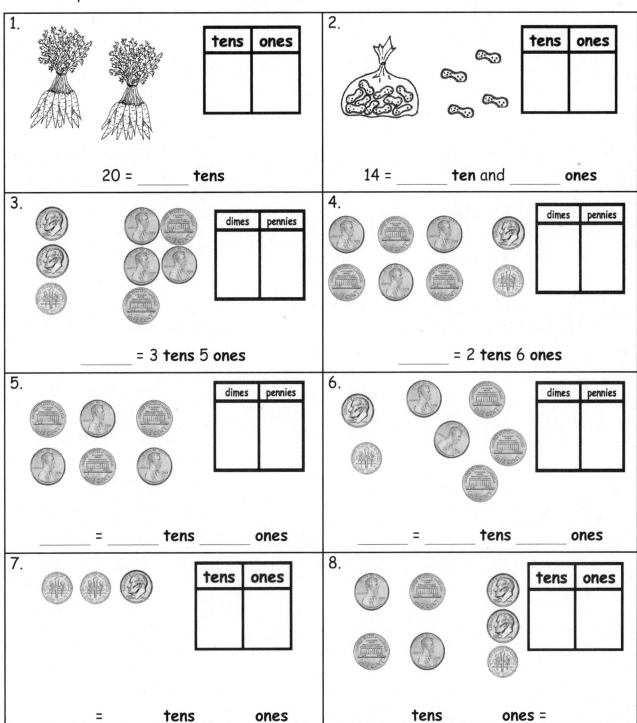

1.

tens	ones

20 = _____ tens

2.

tens	ones

14 = _____ ten and _____ ones

3.

dimes	pennies

_____ = 3 tens 5 ones

4.

dimes	pennies

_____ = 2 tens 6 ones

5.

dimes	pennies

_____ = _____ tens _____ ones

6.

dimes	pennies

_____ = _____ tens _____ ones

7.

tens	ones

_____ = _____ tens _____ ones

8.

tens	ones

_____ tens _____ ones = _____

Lesson 6:   Use dimes and pennies as representations of tens and ones.

39

Fill in the blank. Draw or cross off tens or ones as needed.

10 more than 25 is **35**

9.	10.
1 more than 15 is _____.	10 more than 5 is _____.

11.	12.
10 more than 30 is _____.	1 more than 30 is _____.

13.	14.
1 less than 24 is _____.	10 less than 24 is _____.

15.	16.
10 less than 21 is _____.	1 less than 21 is _____.

Lesson 6:   Use dimes and pennies as representations of tens and ones.

EUREKA MATH

Name _____   Date _____

Fill in the blank. Draw or cross off tens or ones as needed.

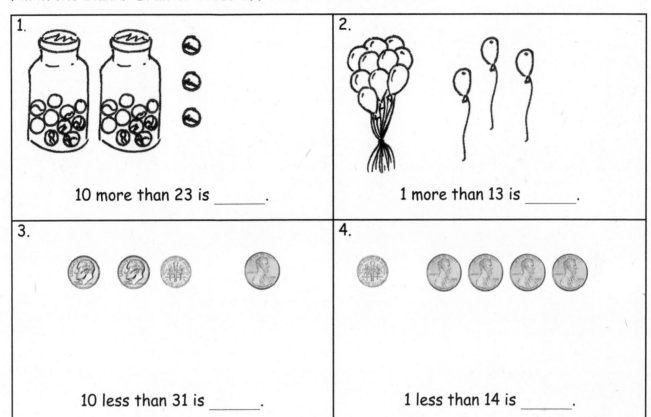

1.

10 more than 23 is _____.

2.

1 more than 13 is _____.

3.

10 less than 31 is _____.

4.

1 less than 14 is _____.

EUREKA
MATH®

Lesson 6:   Use dimes and pennies as representations of tens and ones.

41

© 2018 Great Minds®. eureka-math.org

dimes	pennies

tens	ones

coin and place value charts

Read

Benny has 4 dimes. Marcus has 4 pennies. Bennie says, "We have the same amount of money!" Is he correct? Use drawings or words to explain your thinking.

Draw

Lesson 7:   Compare two quantities, and identify the greater or lesser of the two given numerals.

© 2018 Great Minds®. eureka-math.org

45

Write

_____

_____

_____

Lesson 7:   Compare two quantities, and identify the greater or lesser of the two given numerals.

EUREKA
MATH

Name _____   Date _____

For each pair, write the number of items in each set. Then, circle the set with the *greater* number of items.

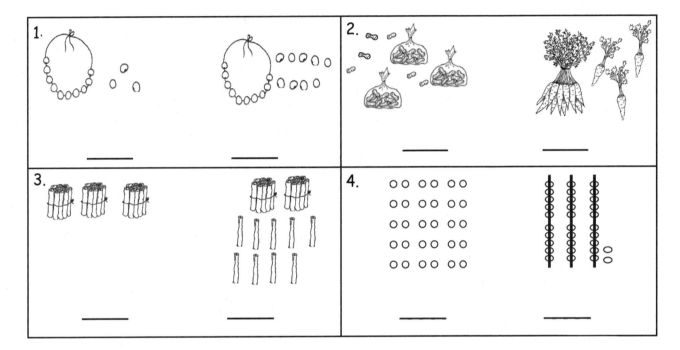

5. Circle the number that is *greater* in each pair.

a. 1 ten 2 ones   3 tens 2 ones

b. 2 tens 8 ones   3 tens 2 ones

c.   19   15

d.   31   26

6. Circle the set of coins that has a *greater* value.

3 dimes   3 pennies

Lesson 7:   Compare two quantities, and identify the greater or lesser of the two
given numerals.

For each pair, write the number of items in each set. Circle the set with *fewer* items.

7.	8.
_____ _____	_____ _____

9.	10.
_____ _____	_____ _____

11. Circle the number that is *less* in each pair.

    a. 2 tens 5 ones   1 ten 5 ones

    b. 28 ones   3 tens 2 ones

    c.   18   13

    d.   31   26

12. Circle the set of coins that has *less* value.

    1 dime 2 pennies   1 penny 2 dimes

13. Circle the amount that is *less*. Draw or write to show how you know.

                              32   17

        Lesson 7:   Compare two quantities, and identify the greater or lesser of the two given numerals.

EUREKA MATH®

Name _____   Date _____

1. Write the number of items in each set. Then, circle the set that is *greater* in number. Write a statement to compare the two sets.

   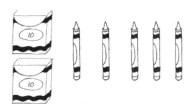

_____   _____

_____ is greater than _____.

2. Write the number of items in each set. Then, circle the set that is *less* in number. Say a statement to compare the two sets.

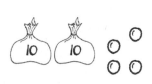   

_____   _____

_____ is less than _____.

3. Circle the set of coins that has a greater value.

4. Circle the set of coins that has less value.

Read

Anton picked 25 strawberries. He picked some more strawberries.

Then, he had 35 strawberries.

   a. Use a place value chart to show how many more strawberries

      Anton picked.

   b. Write a statement comparing the two amounts of strawberries using

      one of these phrases: *greater than, less than,* or *equal to.*

Draw

Lesson 8:   Compare quantities and numerals form left to right.

© 2018 Great Minds®. eureka-math.org

51

Write

Lesson 8:   Compare quantities and numerals form left to right.

EUREKA
MATH

Name _____   Date _____

1. Draw quick tens and ones to show each number. Label the first
    drawing as *less than (L), greater than (G)*, or *equal to (E)* the
    second. Write a phrase from the word bank to compare
    the numbers.

Word Bank

| is greater than |
| is less than |
| is equal to |

a.	b. 2 tens 3tens
20 _____ 18	2 tens _____ 3 tens
c. 24 15	d. 26 32
24 _____ 15	26 _____ 32

2. Write a phrase from the word bank to compare the numbers.

36 _____ 3 tens 6 ones

1 ten 8 ones _____ 3 tens 1 one

38 _____ 26

1 ten 7 ones _____ 27

15 _____ 1 ten 2 ones

30 _____ 28

29 _____ 32

3. Put the following numbers in order from *least* to *greatest*. Cross off each number after it has been used.

9	40	32	13	23

4. Put the following numbers in order from *greatest* to *least*. Cross off each number after it has been used.

9	40	32	13	23

5. Use the digits 8, 3, 2, and 7 to make 4 different two-digit numbers less than 40. Write them in order from *greatest* to *least*.

8	3	2	7

Examples: 32, 27,...

Lesson 8:   Compare quantities and numerals form left to right.

© 2018 Great Minds®. eureka-math.org

EUREKA MATH

Name _____   Date _____

1. Write the numbers in order from *greatest* to *least*.

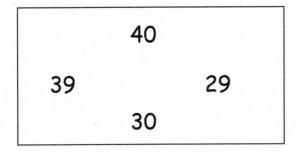

   ___ ___ ___ ___

2. Complete the sentence frames using the phrases from the word bank to compare the two numbers.

   Word Bank

   | is greater than |
   | is less than |
   | is equal to |

   a. 17 _____ 24

   b. 23 _____ 2 tens 3 ones

   c. 29 _____ 20

EUREKA MATH

Lesson 8:   Compare quantities and numerals form left to right.

© 2018 Great Minds®. eureka-math.org

55

Read

Carl has a collection of rocks. He collects 10 more rocks. Now he has 31 rocks. How many rocks did he have in the beginning?

   a. Use place value charts to show how many rocks Carl had at the beginning.

   b. Write a statement comparing how many rocks Carl started and ended with, using one of these phrases: *greater than, less than,* or *equal to.*

Draw

Write

_____

_____

_____

EUREKA MATH

Name _____   Date _____

1. Circle the alligator that is eating the *greater* number.

a.	b.	c.	d.
40 20	10 30	18 14	19 36

2. Write the numbers in the blanks so that the alligator is eating the *greater* number. With a partner, compare the numbers out loud, using *is greater than*, *less than*, or *is equal to*. Remember to start with the number on the left.

a.	b.	c.
24 4	38 36	_ 14
___ > ___	___ < ___	___ < ___

d.	e.	f.
20 2	36 35	20 19
___ > ___	___ < ___	___ > ___

g.	h.	i.
31 13	23 32	21 12
___ > ___	___ < ___	___ < ___

EUREKA MATH

Lesson 9:   Use the symbols >, =, and < to compare quantities and numerals.

59

© 2018 Great Minds®. eureka-math.org

3. If the alligator is eating the *greater* number, circle it. If not, redraw the alligator.

a.			b.		
20	>	19	32	<	23

4. Complete the charts so that the alligator is eating a *greater* number.

	tens	ones		tens	ones		tens	ones		tens	ones
a.	1	2	>	1		b.	2	7	>	2	
c.	2	5	>		5	d.		8	<	3	8
e.	2	1	>	2		f.	2	4	<		4
g.	1	8	>		5	h.	2	1	>		9
i.		7	<	2	1	j.	1	4	>		4

EUREKA MATH

Name _____   Date _____

Write the numbers in the blanks so that the alligator is eating the greater number. Read the number sentence, using *is greater than, is less than,* or *is equal to*. Remember to start with the number on the left.

a. 12 10 ___ > ___	b. 22 24 ___ < ___	c. 17 25 ___ > ___
d. 13 3 ___ > ___	e. 27 28 ___ > ___	f. 30 21 ___ < ___
g. 12 21 ___ > ___	h. 31 13 ___ < ___	i. 32 23 ___ < ___

Read

Elaine and Mike were picking blueberries. Elaine had 19 blueberries and ate 10. Mike had 13 and picked 7 more. Compare Elaine and Mike's blueberries after Elaine ate some and Mike picked some more.

  a. Use words and pictures to show how many blueberries each person has.

  b. Use the term *greater than or less than* in your statement.

Draw

Write

_____

_____

_____

EUREKA MATH

Name _____   Date _____

1. Use the symbols to compare the numbers. Fill in the blank with <, >, or = to make a true number sentence. Read the number sentences from left to right.

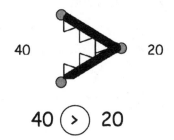

40 (>) 20   18 (<) 20

40 is greater than 20.   18 is less than 20.

a.	b.	c.
27 ◯ 24	31 ◯ 28	10 ◯ 13
d.	e.	f.
13 ◯ 15	31 ◯ 29	38 ◯ 18
g.	h.	i.
27 ◯ 17	32 ◯ 21	12 ◯ 21

© 2018 Great Minds®. eureka-math.org

2. Circle the correct words to make the sentence true. Use >, <, or = and numbers to write a true number sentence. The first one is done for you.

a.

36 | is greater than
       | is less than
       | (is equal to) | 3 tens 6 ones

__36__ (=) __36__

b.

1 ten 4 ones | is greater than
                | is less than
                | is equal to | 17

____ ( ) ____

c.

2 tens 4 ones | is greater than
                 | is less than
                 | is equal to | 34

____ ( ) ____

d.

20 | is greater than
      | is less than
      | is equal to | 2 tens 0 ones

____ ( ) ____

e.

31 | is greater than
      | is less than
      | is equal to | 13

____ ( ) ____

f.

12 | is greater than
      | is less than
      | is equal to | 21

____ ( ) ____

g.

17 | is greater than
      | is less than
      | is equal to | 3 ones 1 ten

____ ( ) ____

h.

30 | is greater than
      | is less than
      | is equal to | 0 tens 30 ones

____ ( ) ____

Lesson 10:   Use the symbols >, =, and < to compare quantities and numerals.

EUREKA MATH

Name _____   Date _____

Circle the correct words to make the sentence true. Use >, <, or = and numbers to write a true number sentence.

a.		
29	is greater than is less than is equal to	2 tens 6 ones

____ ◯ ____

b.		
1 ten 8 ones	is greater than is less than is equal to	19

____ ◯ ____

c.		
2 tens 9 ones	is greater than is less than is equal to	40

____ ◯ ____

d.		
39	is greater than is less than is equal to	4 tens 0 ones

____ ◯ ____

EUREKA MATH®

Lesson 10:   Use the symbols >, =, and < to compare quantities and numerals.

67

© 2018 Great Minds®. eureka-math.org

Read

Sharon has 3 dimes and 1 penny. Mia has 1 dime and 3 pennies. Whose amount of money has a greater value?

Draw

Write

_____

_____

_____

Name _____ Date _____

Complete the number bonds and number sentences to match the picture. The first one is done for you.

1.

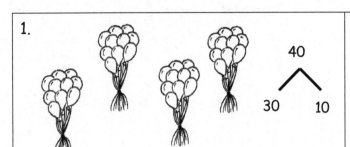

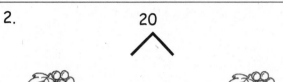

3 tens + 1 ten = 4 tens
30 + 10 = 40

2.

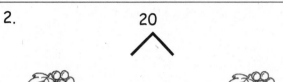

_____ ten + _____ ten = _____ tens

_____

3.

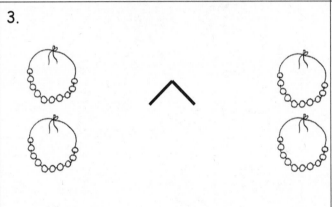

_____ tens = _____ tens + _____ tens

_____

4.

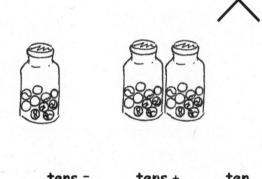

_____ tens = _____ tens + _____ ten

_____

5.

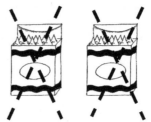

_____ tens - _____ ten = _____ tens

_____

6.

_____ tens - _____ tens = _____ tens

_____

7.

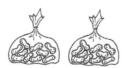

_____ tens + _____ ten = _____ tens

_____

8.

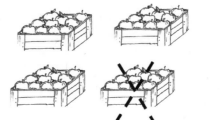

_____ tens - _____ ten = _____ tens

_____ + _____

9.

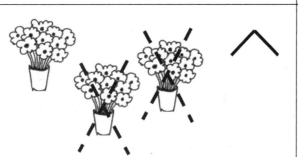

_____ tens - _____ tens = _____ ten

_____

10.

_____ ten - _____ tens = _____ ten

_____

Lesson 11:   Add and subtract tens from a multiple of 10.

EUREKA
MATH®

11. Fill in the missing numbers. Match the related addition and subtraction facts.

   a. 4 tens - 2 tens = _____   2 tens + 1 ten = 3 tens

   b. 40 – 30 = _____   30 + 10 = 40

   c. 30 – 20 = _____   20 + 20 = 40

12. Fill in the missing numbers.

   a. 20 + 20 = _____   b. 30 – 20 = _____   c. 10 + _____ = 40

   d. 20 – _____ = 0   e. 40 – _____ = 10   f. _____ + _____ = 30

Name _____   Date _____

Complete the number bonds and number sentences.

1.

1 ten + 1 ten = _____ tens

_____ + _____ = 20

2.

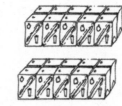 

_____ tens = _____ tens + _____ ten

_____ = _____ + _____

3.

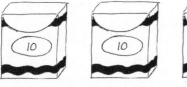

_____ tens - _____ ten = _____ tens

_____ - _____ = _____

4.

_____ tens - _____ tens = _____ tens

_____ - _____ = _____

___ ◯ ____ ◯ ____

____ tens ◯ ____ tens ◯ ____ tens

___ ◯ ____ ◯ ____

number bond/number sentence set

Read

Thomas has a box of paper clips. He used 10 of them to measure the length of his big book. There are 20 paper clips still in the box. Use the arrow way to show how many paper clips were in the box at first.

Draw

Write

_____

_____

_____

Lesson 12:   Add tens to a two-digit number.

EUREKA
MATH

Name _____   Date _____

Fill in the missing numbers to match the picture. Write the matching number bond.

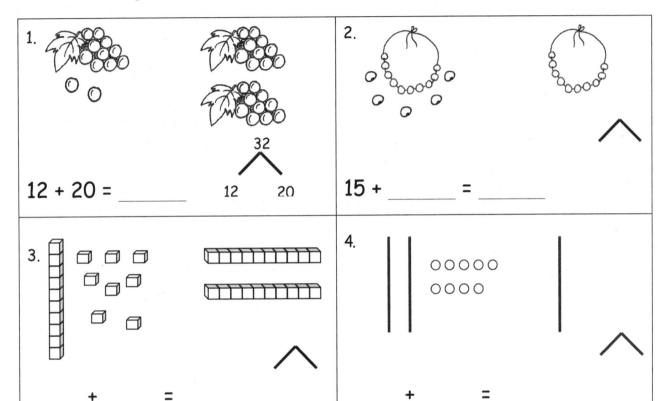

1.

32

12 + 20 = _____   12   20

2.

15 + _____ = _____

3.

_____ + _____ = _____

4.

_____ + _____ = _____

Draw using quick tens and ones. Complete the number bond, and write the sum in the place value chart and the number sentence.

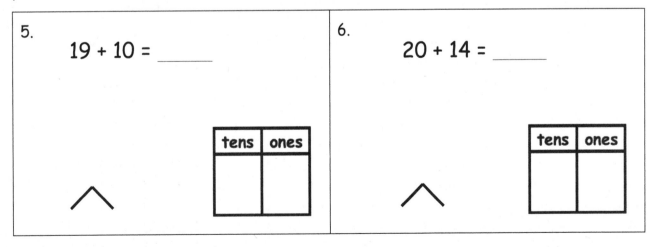

5.

19 + 10 = _____

tens	ones

6.

20 + 14 = _____

tens	ones

Use arrow notation to solve.

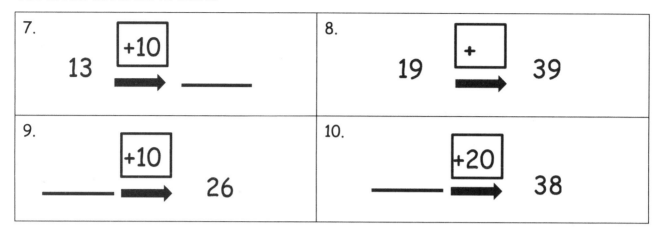

7.

13 [+10] ⟶ _____

8.

19 [+] ⟶ 39

9.

_____ [+10] ⟶ 26

10.

_____ [+20] ⟶ 38

Use the dimes and pennies to complete the place value charts and the number sentences.

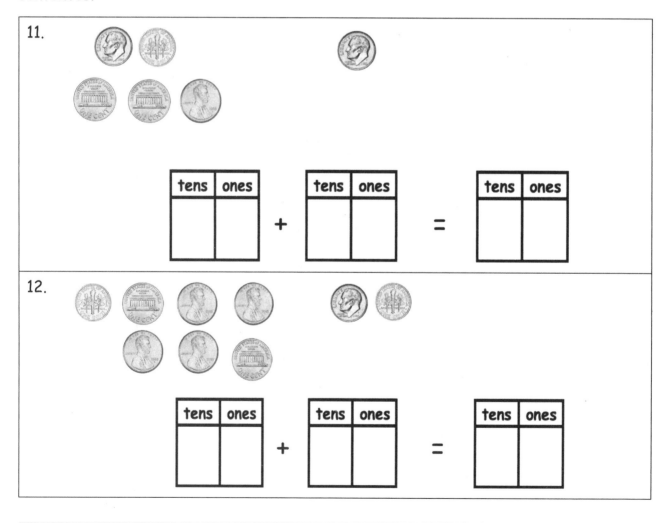

11.

tens	ones		tens	ones		tens	ones
		+			=		

12.

tens	ones		tens	ones		tens	ones
		+			=		

Lesson 12:   Add tens to a two-digit number.

EUREKA
MATH

Name _____   Date _____

Complete the number sentences. Use quick tens, the arrow way, or coins to show your thinking.

28 + 10 = _____

14 + 20 = _____

Use linking cubes as you read, draw, and write (RDW) to solve the problems.

Read

a. Emi had a linking cube train with 4 blue cubes and 2 red cubes. How many cubes were in her train?

b. Emi made another train with 6 yellow cubes and some green cubes. The train was made of 9 linking cubes. How many green cubes did she use?

c. Emi wants to make her train of 9 linking cubes into a train of 15 cubes. How many cubes does Emi need?

Draw

Lesson 13:   Use counting on and the make ten strategy when adding across a ten.

85

© 2018 Great Minds®. eureka-math.org

Write

_____

_____

_____

EUREKA MATH

Name _____   Date _____

Use the pictures to complete the place value chart and number sentence. For Problem 5 and 6, make a quick ten drawing to help you solve.

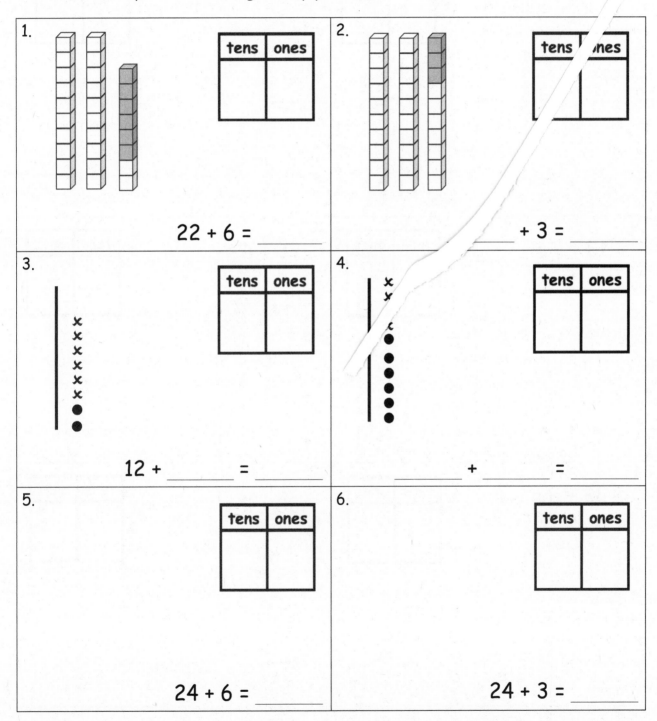

1.

tens	ones

22 + 6 = _____

2.

tens	ones

_____ + 3 = _____

3.

tens	ones

12 + _____ = _____

4.

tens	ones

_____ + _____ = _____

5.

tens	ones

24 + 6 = _____

6.

tens	ones

24 + 3 = _____

EUREKA MATH

Lesson 13:   Use counting on and the make ten strategy when adding across a ten.

87

© 2018 Great Minds®. eureka-math.org

Draw quick tens, ones, and number bonds to solve. Complete the place value chart.

7.

$21 + 9 =$ _____

tens	ones

```
| |  x
| |  x
| |  x
| |  x
| |  x
| |  x
| |  x
| |  x
| |  x
|    ●
```

8.

$21 + 7 =$ _____

tens	ones

9.

$13 + 7 =$ _____

tens	ones

10.

$26 + 4 =$ _____

tens	ones

11.

$32 + 3 =$ _____

tens	ones

12.

$38 + 2 =$ _____

tens	ones

Lesson 13:   Use counting on and the make ten strategy when adding across a ten.

© 2018 Great Minds®. eureka-math.org

EUREKA MATH

Name _____   Date _____

Fill in the place value chart, and write a number sentence to match the picture.

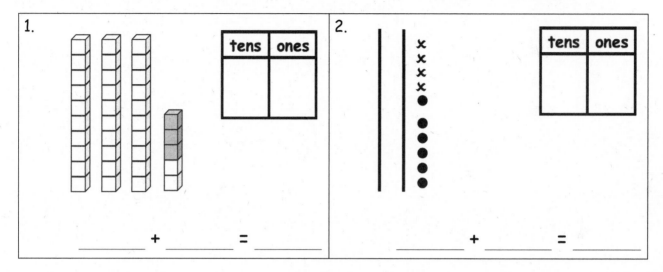

1.

tens	ones

_____ + _____ = _____

2.

tens	ones

_____ + _____ = _____

Draw quick tens, ones, and number bonds to solve. Complete the place value chart.

3.

33 + 6 = _____

tens	ones

4.

23 + 7 = _____

tens	ones

Use linking cubes and the RDW process to solve one or more of the problems.

Read

a. Emi had a linking cube train of 7 cubes. She added 4 cubes to the train. How many cubes are in her linking cube train?

b. Emi made another train of linking cubes. She started with 7 cubes and added some more cubes until her train was 9 cubes long. How many cubes did Emi add?

c. Emi made one more train of linking cubes. It was made of 8 linking cubes. She took some cubes off, and then her train was 4 linking cubes long. How many cubes did Emi take off?

Draw

Write

_____

_____

_____

Lesson 14:   Use counting on and the make ten strategy when adding across a ten.

EUREKA
MATH®

Name _____ Date _____

Use the pictures or draw quick tens and ones. Complete the number sentence and place value chart.

1.	2.	3.
18 + 1 = _____ 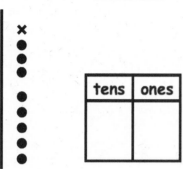 tens | ones	18 + 2 = _____ 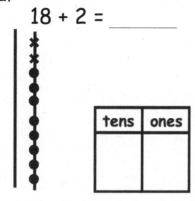 tens | ones	18 + 5 = _____ 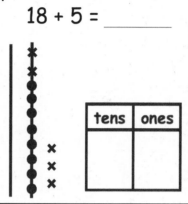 tens | ones
4. 29 + 1 = _____ tens | ones	5. 29 + 3 = _____ tens | ones	6. 29 + 6 = _____ tens | ones
7. 16 + 4 = _____ tens | ones	8. 16 + 6 = _____ tens | ones	9. 26 + 6 = _____ tens | ones

EUREKA MATH®

Lesson 14: Use counting on and the make ten strategy when adding across a ten.

93

Make a number bond to ___ve. Show your thinking with number sentences or the arrow way. Complete the pla__ value chart.

10.

$17 + 2 =$ _____

tens	ones

11.

$17 + 5 =$ _____

tens	ones

12.

$25 \quad 4 =$ _____

tens	ones

13.

$25 + 6 =$ _____

tens	ones

14.

$34 + 4 =$ _____

tens	ones

15.

$34 + 8 =$ _____

tens	ones

Lesson 14: Use counting on and the make ten strategy when adding across a ten.

EUREKA MATH

Name _____ Date _____

Draw quick tens and ones. Complete the number sentence and place value chart.

1.	2.	3.
17 + 1 = _____	17 + 3 = _____	17 + 6 = _____
tens | ones	tens | ones	tens | ones

Make a number bond to solve. Show your thinking with number sentences or the arrow way. Complete the place value chart.

4.	5.
32 + 7 = _____ tens | ones	26 + 9 = _____ tens | ones

EUREKA MATH

Lesson 14:   Use counting on and the make ten strategy when adding across a ten.

95

© 2018 Great Minds®. eureka-math.org

Use the RDW process to solve one or more of the problems.

Read

a. Emi had a linking cube train of 6 cubes. She added 3 cubes to the train. How many cubes are in her linking cube train?

b. Emi made another train of linking cubes. She started with 7 cubes and added some more cubes until her train was 12 cubes long. How many cubes did Emi add?

c. Emi made one more train of linking cubes. It was made of 12 linking cubes. She took some cubes off, and then her train became 4 linking cubes long. How many cubes did Emi take off?

Draw

Lesson 15: Use single-digit sums to support solutions for analogous sums to 40.

97

© 2018 Great Minds®. eureka-math.org

Write

Lesson 15:   Use single-digit sums to support solutions for analogous sums to 40.

© 2018 Great Minds®. eureka-math.org

EUREKA
MATH®

Name _____   Date _____

Solve the problems.

1.

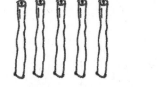

$5 + 3 = $ _____

2.

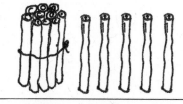

$15 + 3 = $ _____

3.

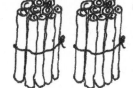 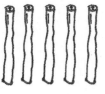 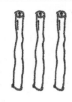

$25 + 3 = $ _____

4.

$35 + 3 = $ _____

5.

$8 + 4 = $ _____

6.

$18 + 4 = $ _____

7.

$28 + 4 = $ _____

EUREKA MATH®

Lesson 15:   Use single-digit sums to support solutions for analogous sums to 40.

99

© 2018 Great Minds®. eureka-math.org

8. Solve the problems.

a. 6 + 2 = ____	b. 16 + 2 = ____	c. 26 + 2 = ____	d. 36 + 2 = ____
e. 6 + 4 = ____	f. 16 + 4 = ____	g. 26 + 4 = ____	h. 36 + 4 = ____
i. 9 + 2 = ____	j. 19 + 2 = ____	k. 29 + 2 = ____	
l. 8 + 6 = ____	m. 18 + 6 = ____	n. 28 + 6 = ____	

Solve the problems. Show the 1-digit addition sentence that helped you solve.

9. 23 + 6 = _____   _____

10. 27 + 6 = _____   _____

Lesson 15:   Use single-digit sums to support solutions for analogous sums to 40.

EUREKA
MATH®

Use the RDW process to solve one or more of the problems without using linking cubes.

Read

a. Emi had a linking cube train with 14 blue cubes and 2 red cubes. How many cubes were in her train?

b. Emi made another train with 16 yellow cubes and some green cubes. The train was made of 19 linking cubes. How many green cubes did she use?

c. Emi wants to make her train of 8 linking cubes into a train of 17 cubes. How many cubes does Emi need?

Draw

Write

_____

_____

_____

Lesson 16: Add ones and ones or tens and tens.

EUREKA
MATH

Name _____ Date _____

Draw quick tens and ones to help you solve the addition problems.

1. $16 + 3 =$ ___	2. $17 + 3 =$ ___
3. $18 + 20 =$ ___	4. $31 + 8 =$ ___
5. $3 + 14 =$ ___	6. $6 + 30 =$ ___
7. $23 + 7 =$ ___	8. $17 + 3 =$ ___

With a partner, try more problems using quick ten drawings, number bonds, or the arrow way.

9. 32 + 7 = _____

10. 13 + 20 = _____

11. 6 + 34 = _____

12. 4 + 36 = _____

13. 20 + 18 = _____

14. 14 + 20 = _____

15. Draw dimes and pennies to help you solve the addition problems.

a. 16 + 20 = _____	b. 22 + 7 = _____

Lesson 16:   Add ones and ones or tens and tens.

EUREKA
MATH®

Name _____ Date _____

Solve using quick ten drawings to show your work.

1. 24 + 5	2. 14 + 20

Draw number bonds to solve.

3. 19 + 20	4. 36 + 3

5. Draw dimes and pennies to help you solve the addition problem.

13 + 20

Use the RDW process to solve one or more of the problems.

Read

    a. Ben had 7 fish. He bought 4 fish at the store. How many fish does Ben have?

    b. Maria had 7 fish in her tank this morning. She bought some more fish, and now she has 9. How many fish did she buy?

    c. Anton had 8 fish. Some of the fish died, and now Anton has 4 fish. How many fish died?

Draw

Write

_____

_____

_____

EUREKA MATH

Name _____   Date _____

Solve the problems by drawing quick tens and ones or a number bond.

1. 25 + 1 = _____	2. 25 + 10 = _____
3. 15 + 4 = _____	4. 15 + 20 = _____
5. 16 + 7 = _____	6. 26 + 7 = _____
7. 23 + 7 = _____	8. 33 + 7 = _____

9. $16 + 20 = $ _____	10. $6 + 24 = $ _____

11. Try more problems with a partner. Use your personal white board to help you solve.

   a. 4 + 26   b. 28 + 4

   c. 32 + 7   d. 20 + 18

   e. 9 + 23   f. 9 + 27

Choose one problem you solved by drawing quick tens, and be ready to discuss.

Choose one problem you solved using the number bond, and be ready to discuss.

EUREKA
MATH

Name _____   Date _____

Find the totals using quick ten drawings or number bonds.

1. 17 + 8 = _____	2. 28 + 7 = _____
3. 24 + 10 = _____	4. 19 + 20 = _____

Use the RDW process to solve one or both of the problems.

Read

a. Some ducks were in a pond. 4 baby ducks joined them. Now, there are 6 ducks in the pond. How many ducks were in the pond at first?

b. Some frogs were in a pond. Three jumped out, and now there are 5 frogs in the pond. How many frogs were in the pond at first?

Draw

Lesson 18:   Share and critique peer strategies for adding two-digit numbers.

115

Write

_____

_____

_____

Share and critique peer strategies for adding two-digit numbers.

EUREKA
MATH

Name _____ Date _____

1. Each of the solutions is missing numbers or parts of the drawing. Fix each one so it is accurate and complete.

13 + 8 = 21

a.   b.   c.

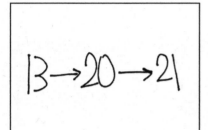   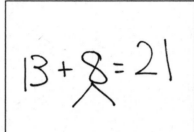   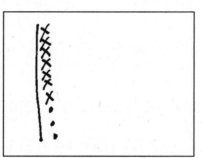

2. Circle the student work that correctly solves the addition problem.

16 + 5

a.   b.   c.

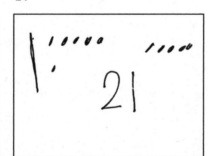   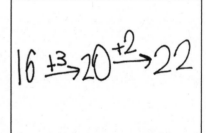

d. Fix the work that was incorrect by making new work in the space below with the matching number sentence.

3. Circle the student work that correctly solves the addition problem.

13 + 20

a.

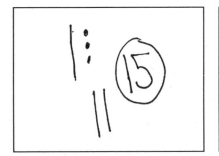

b.

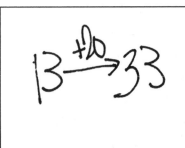

c.

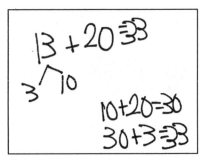

d. Fix the work that was incorrect by making a new drawing in the space below with the matching number sentence.

4. Solve using quick tens, the arrow way, or number bonds.

17 + 5 = _____

Share with your partner. Discuss why you chose to solve the way you did.

Name _____   Date _____

Circle the work that correctly solves the addition problem.

17 + 9

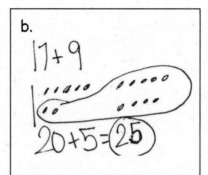

a.

17 + 9
3   6

17 + 3 = 20
20 + 6 = 26

b.

17 + 9

20 + 5 = (25)

c.

17 + 9

17 $\xrightarrow{+3}$ 20 $\xrightarrow{+6}$ 26

d.   Fix the work that was incorrect by making a new drawing in the space below with the matching number sentence.

EUREKA MATH

Lesson 18:   Share and critique peer strategies for adding two-digit numbers.

119

© 2018 Great Minds®. eureka-math.org

Name _____   Date _____

Read the word problem.
Draw a tape diagram and label.
Write a number sentence and a statement that matches
the story.

1. Lee saw 6 squashes and 7 pumpkins growing in his garden. How many vegetables did
   he see growing in his garden?

                                    Lee saw _____ vegetables.

2. Kiana caught 6 lizards. Her brother caught 6 snakes. How many reptiles do they
   have altogether?

                         Kiana and her brother have _____ reptiles.

3. Anton's team has 12 soccer balls on the field and 3 soccer balls in the coach's bag.
   How many soccer balls does Anton's team have?

                              Anton's team has _____ soccer balls.

EUREKA
MATH®

Lesson 19:   Use tape diagrams as representations to solve *put together/take apart*
              with total unknown and *add to with result unknown* word problems.

121

© 2018 Great Minds®. eureka-math.org

4. Emi had 13 friends over for dinner. 4 more friends came over for cake. How many friends came over to Emi's house?

There were _____ friends.

5. 6 adults and 12 children were swimming in the lake. How many people were swimming in the lake?

There were _____ people swimming in the lake.

6. Rose has a vase with 13 flowers. She puts 7 more flowers in the vase. How many flowers are in the vase?

There are _____ flowers in the vase.

Lesson 19:   Use tape diagrams as representations to solve *put together/take apart with total unknown* and *add to with result unknown* word problems.

© 2018 Great Minds®. eureka-math.org

EUREKA
MATH

Name _____ Date _____

Read the word problem.
Draw a tape diagram and label.
Write a number sentence and a statement that matches the story.

16

12   4
ooooooooooo●●   ●●●●

Peter counted 14 ladybugs in a garden, and Lee counted 6 ladybugs outside of the garden. How many ladybugs did they count in all?

They counted _____ ladybugs.

Lesson 19:   Use tape diagrams as representations to solve *put together/take apart with total unknown* and *add to with result unknown* word problems.

© 2018 Great Minds®. eureka-math.org

123

Name _____   Date _____

Read the word problem.
Draw a tape diagram and label.
Write a number sentence and a statement that matches
the story.

1. 9 dogs were playing at the park. Some more dogs came to the park. Then, there
    were 11 dogs. How many more dogs came to the park?

    _____ more dogs came to the park.

2. 16 strawberries are in a basket for Peter and Julio. Peter eats 8 of them. How
    many are there for Julio to eat?

    Julio has _____ strawberries to eat.

3. 13 children are on the roller coaster. 3 adults are on the roller coaster. How many
    people are on the roller coaster?

    There are _____ people on the roller coaster.

EUREKA MATH

Lesson 20:   Recognize and make use of part–whole relationships within tape
               diagrams when solving a variety of problem types.

© 2018 Great Minds®. eureka-math.org

125

4. 13 people are on the roller coaster now. 3 adults are on the roller coaster, and the rest are children. How many children are on the roller coaster?

There are _____ children on the roller coaster.

5. Ben has 6 baseball practices in the morning this month. If Ben also has 6 practices in the afternoon, how many baseball practices does Ben have?

Ben has _____ baseball practices.

6. Some yellow beads were on Tamra's bracelet. After she put 14 purple beads on the bracelet, there were 18 beads. How many yellow beads did Tamra's bracelet have at first?

Tamra's bracelet had _____ yellow beads.

Lesson 20:   Recognize and make use of part–whole relationships within tape
diagrams when solving a variety of problem types.

© 2018 Great Minds®. eureka-math.org

EUREKA
MATH®

Name _____ Date _____

Read the word problem.
Draw a tape diagram and label.
Write a number sentence and a statement that matches
the story.

16

12
0000000000●● | 4 ●●●●

There were 6 turtles in the tank. Dad bought some more turtles. Now, there are
12 turtles. How many turtles did Dad buy?

Dad bought _____ turtles.

Lesson 20:   Recognize and make use of part–whole relationships within tape
diagrams when solving a variety of problem types.

127

Name _____ Date _____

<u>R</u>ead the word problem.
<u>D</u>raw a tape diagram and label.
<u>W</u>rite a number sentence and a statement that matches the story.

1. Rose drew 7 pictures, and Willie drew 11 pictures. How many pictures did they draw all together?

    They drew _____ pictures.

2. Darnel walked 7 minutes to Lee's house. Then, he walked to the park. Darnel walked for a total of 18 minutes. How many minutes did it take Darnel to get to the park?

    It took Darnel _____ minutes to get to the park.

3. Emi has some goldfish. Tamra has 14 betta fish. Tamra and Emi have 19 fish in all. How many goldfish does Emi have?

    Emi has _____ goldfish.

EUREKA
MATH®

Lesson 21:   Recognize and make use of part–whole relationships within tape
diagrams when solving a variety of problem types.

129

© 2018 Great Minds®. eureka-math.org

4. Shanika built a block tower using 14 blocks. Then, she added 4 more blocks to the tower. How many blocks are there in the tower now?

The tower is made of _____ blocks.

5. Nikil's tower is 15 blocks tall. He added some more blocks to his tower. His tower is 18 blocks tall now. How many blocks did Nikil add?

Nikil added _____ blocks.

6. Ben and Peter caught 17 tadpoles. They gave some to Anton. They have 4 tadpoles left. How many tadpoles did they give to Anton?

They gave Anton _____ tadpoles.

Recognize and make use of part–whole relationships within tape diagrams when solving a variety of problem types.

EUREKA MATH®

Name _____ Date _____

Read the word problem.
Draw a tape diagram and label.
Write a number sentence and a statement that matches
the story.

Shanika read some pages on Monday. On Tuesday, she read 6 pages. She read 13 pages
during the 2 days. How many pages did she read on Monday?

                            Shanika read _____ pages on Monday.

Lesson 21:   Recognize and make use of part–whole relationships within tape
              diagrams when solving a variety of problem types.

© 2018 Great Minds®. eureka-math.org

131

Name _____   Date _____

Use the tape diagrams to write a variety of word problems. Use the word bank
if needed. Remember to label your model after you write the story.

Topics (Nouns)		
flowers	goldfish	lizards
stickers	rockets	cars
frogs	crackers	marbles

Actions (Verbs)		
hide	eat	go away
give	draw	get
collect	build	play

1.

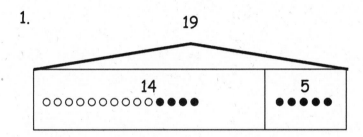

2.

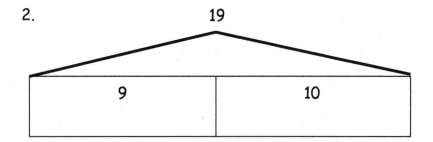

EUREKA
MATH

3.

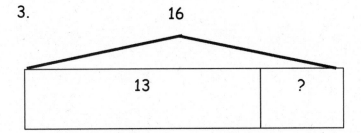

4.

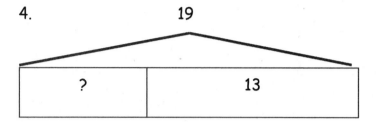

EUREKA
MATH

Name _____ Date _____

Circle the 2 story problems that match the tape diagram.

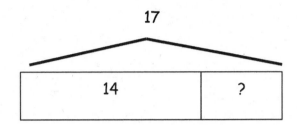

a. There are 14 ants on the picnic blanket. Then, some more ants came over. Now, there are 17 ants on the picnic blanket. How many ants came over?

b. 14 children are on the playground from one class. Then, 17 children from another class came to the playground. How many children are on the playground now?

c. 17 grapes were on the plate. Willie ate 14 grapes. How many grapes are on the plate now?

Read

Kim picks up 10 loose pencils and puts them in a cup. Ben has 1 package of 10 pencils that he adds to the cup. How many pencils are now in the cup?

Draw

Write

_____

_____

_____

Lesson 23:   Interpret two-digit numbers as tens and ones, including cases with more than 9 ones.

139

© 2018 Great Minds®. eureka-math.org

Name _____ Date _____

1. Fill in the blanks, and match the pairs that show the same amount.

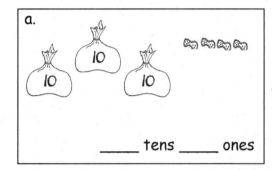

a. _____ tens _____ ones

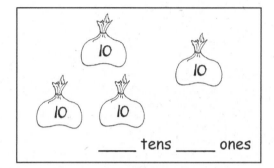

_____ tens _____ ones

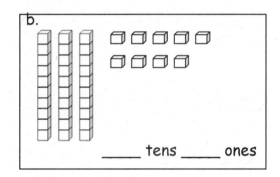

b. _____ tens _____ ones

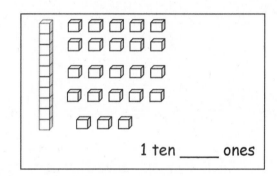

1 ten _____ ones

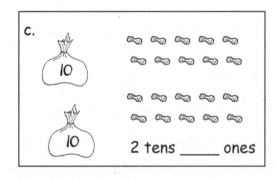

c. 2 tens _____ ones

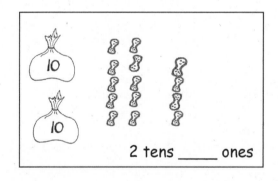

2 tens _____ ones

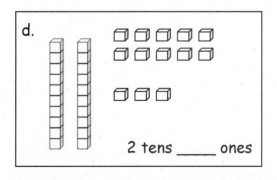

d. 2 tens _____ ones

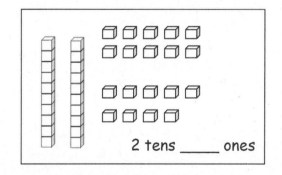

2 tens _____ ones

EUREKA MATH

Lesson 23: Interpret two-digit numbers as tens and ones, including cases with more than 9 ones.

141

© 2018 Great Minds®. eureka-math.org

2. Match the place value charts that show the same amount.

a.
tens	ones
2	2

tens	ones
3	6

b.
tens	ones
2	16

tens	ones
3	4

c.
tens	ones
2	14

tens	ones
1	12

3. Check each sentence that is true.

☐ a. 27 is the same as 1 ten 17 ones. ☐ b. 33 is the same as 2 tens 23 ones.

☐ c. 37 is the same as 2 tens 17 ones. ☐ d. 29 is the same as 1 ten 19 ones.

4. Lee says that 35 is the same as 2 tens 15 ones, and Maria says that 35 is the same as 1 ten 25 ones. Draw quick tens to show if either Lee or Maria is correct.

Lesson 23:   Interpret two-digit numbers as tens and ones, including cases with more than 9 ones.

© 2018 Great Minds®. eureka-math.org

EUREKA MATH

Name _____   Date _____

1. Match the place value charts that show the same amount.

a.

tens	ones
2	12

tens	ones
2	16

b.

tens	ones
2	8

tens	ones
1	18

c.

tens	ones
3	6

tens	ones
3	2

2. Tamra says that 24 is the same as 1 ten 14 ones, and Willie says that 24 is the same as 2 tens 14 ones. Draw quick tens to show if Tamra or Willie is correct.

EUREKA MATH

Lesson 23:   Interpret two-digit numbers as tens and ones, including cases with more than 9 ones.

© 2018 Great Minds®. eureka-math.org

143

Read

A dog hides 11 bones behind his doghouse. Later, his owner gives him 5 more bones. How many bones does the dog have now?

Extension: All the bones are brown or white. The same number of bones are brown as white. How many brown bones does the dog have?

Draw

EUREKA MATH   Lesson 24:   Add a pair of two-digit numbers when the ones digits have a sum less than or equal to 10.   145

© 2018 Great Minds®. eureka-math.org

Write

_____

_____

_____

Add a pair of two-digit numbers when the ones digits have a sum less than or equal to 10.

EUREKA MATH®

Name _____   Date _____

1. Solve using number bonds. Write the two number sentences that show that you added the ten first. Draw quick tens and ones if that helps you.

a.	b.
$14 + 13 =$ ____ $\wedge$ 10 3 $14 + 10 = 24$ $24 + 3 = 27$	$13 + 24 =$ ____ $\wedge$ 10 3 $24 + 10 =$ ____ ____ $+ 3 =$ ____
c.	d.
$16 + 13 =$ ____ $\wedge$ 10 3 $16 + 10 =$ ____ ____ $+ 3 =$ ____	$13 + 26 =$ ____ $\wedge$ 10 3 $26 + 10 =$ ____ ____ $+$ ____ $=$ ____
e.	f.
$15 + 15 =$ ____ $\wedge$ 10 5 ____ $+$ ____ $=$ ____ ____ $+$ ____ $=$ ____	$15 + 25 =$ ____ $\wedge$ ____ $+$ ____ $=$ ____ ____ $+$ ____ $=$ ____

EUREKA MATH

Lesson 24:   Add a pair of two-digit numbers when the ones digits have a sum less than or equal to 10.

© 2018 Great Minds®. eureka-math.org

147

2. Solve using number bonds or the arrow way. Part (a) has been started for y

a. 15 + 13 = ____ 10 3	b. 14 + 23 = ____
c. 16 + 14 = ____	d. 14 + 26 = ____
e. 21 + 17 = ____	f. 17 + 23 = ____
g. 21 + 18 = ____	h. 18 + 12 = ____

Lesson 24:   Add a pair of two-digit numbers when the ones digits have a sum less
than or equal to 10.

EUREKA
MATH

Name _____   Date _____

Solve using number bonds. Write the two number sentences that show that you added the ten first.

1. 13 + 26 = _____ + _____ = _____ _____ + _____ = _____	2. 19 + 21 = _____ + _____ = _____ _____ + _____ = _____

Read

A chipmunk hides 11 acorns under a tree. Later, he gives 5 of the acorns to his friend. How many acorns does the chipmunk have?

Extension: A squirrel has double the number of acorns the chipmunk had to begin with. How many acorns does the squirrel have?

Draw

Lesson 25:   Add a pair of two-digit numbers when the ones digits have a sum less than or equal to 10.

© 2018 Great Minds®. eureka-math.org

151

Write

_____

_____

_____

Lesson 25:   Add a pair of two-digit numbers when the ones digits have a sum less than or equal to 10.

© 2018 Great Minds®. eureka-math.org

EUREKA
MATH®

Name _____ Date _____

1. Solve using number bonds. This time, add the tens first. Write the 2 number sentences to show what you did.

a. 11 + 14 = _____	b. 21 + 14 = _____
c. 14 + 15 = _____	d. 26 + 14 = _____
e. 26 + 13 = _____	f. 13 + 24 = _____

Lesson 25:   Add a pair of two-digit numbers when the ones digits have a sum less than or equal to 10.

© 2018 Great Minds®. eureka-math.org

153

2. Solve using number bonds. This time, add the ones first. Write the 2 number sentences to show what you did.

a. 29 + 11 = _____	b. 17 + 13 = _____
c. 14 + 16 = _____	d. 26 + 13 = _____
e. 28 + 11 = _____	f. 12 + 27 = _____
g. 18 + 12 = _____	h. 22 + 18 = _____

Lesson 25:   Add a pair of two-digit numbers when the ones digits have a sum less than or equal to 10.

© 2018 Great Minds®. eureka-math.org

EUREKA MATH

Name _____   Date _____

Solve using number bonds. Write the 2 number sentences to record what you did.

a.	b.
12 + 27 = _____	21 + 19 = _____

Lesson 25:   Add a pair of two-digit numbers when the ones digits have a sum less
               than or equal to 10.

© 2018 Great Minds®. eureka-math.org

155

Read

It snowed 7 days in February and the same number of days in March. How many days did it snow in those 2 months?

Extension: It snowed 3 days in January. How many days did it snow in all 3 months? How many more days did it snow in February than in January?

Draw

Lesson 26:   Add a pair of two-digit numbers when the ones digits have a sum greater than 10.

© 2018 Great Minds®. eureka-math.org

157

Write

_____

_____

_____

Lesson 26:   Add a pair of two-digit numbers when the ones digits have a sum greater than 10.

© 2018 Great Minds®. eureka-math.org

Name _____   Date _____

1. Solve using a number bond to add ten first. Write the 2 addition sentences that helped you.

a. 18 + 14 = _____ ∧ 10 4 18 + 10 = 28 28 + 4 = 32	b. 1 ̇ 17 = _____ ∧ 10 4 _ + 10 = 27 27 ̇ = 31
c. 19 + 15 = _____ ∧ 10 5 19 + 10 = _____ _____ + 5 = _____	d. 18 + 15 = _____ ∧ 10 5 18 + 10 = _____ _____ + 5 = _____
e. 19 + 13 = _____ ∧ 10 3 19 + 10 = _____ _____ + _____ = _____	f. 19 + 16 = _____ ∧ 10 6 19 + 10 = _____ _____ + _____ = _____

2. Solve using a number bond to make a ten first. Write the 2 number sentences that helped you.

a. 19 + 14 = _____ ∧ 1 13 19 + 1 = 20 20 + 13 = 33	b. 18 + 13 = _____ ∧ 2 11 18 + 2 = 20 20 + 11 = 31
c. 18 + 14 = _____ ∧ 2 12 18 + 2 = _____ 20 + 12 = _____	d. 18 + 16 = _____ ∧ 2 14 18 + 2 = _____ _____ + 14 = _____
e. 15 + 17 = _____ ∧ 12 3 _____ + 3 = _____ _____ + 12 = _____	f. 17 + 18 = _____ ∧ 15 2 _____ + _____ = _____ _____ + _____ = _____

Lesson 26:   Add a pair of two-digit numbers when the ones digits have a sum greater than 10.

© 2018 Great Minds®. eureka-math.org

EUREKA MATH

Name _____   Date _____

1. Solve using number bonds to add ten first. Write the 2 number sentences that helped you.

a. 15 + 19 = _____ ∧ ____ + ____ = ____ ____ + ____ = ____	b. 19 + 17 = _____ ∧ ____ + ____ = ____ ____ + ____ = ____

2. Solve using number bonds to make a ten. Write the 2 number sentences that helped you.

a. 15 + 19 = _____ ∧ ____ + ____ = ____ ____ + ____ = ____	b. 19 + 17 = _____ ∧ ____ + ____ = ____ ____ + ____ = ____

Read

During the winter, it snowed on 14 different days. On some of the days, we got to stay home. For 9 of the snowy days, we had to go to school. For how many days did we get to stay home?

Extension: How many more days did it snow when we were in school compared to when we were home?

Draw

Lesson 27:   Add a pair of two-digit numbers when the ones digits have a sum greater than 10.

163

© 2018 Great Minds®. eureka-math.org

Write

_____

_____

_____

Add a pair of two-digit numbers when the ones digits have a sum greater than 10.

EUREKA MATH

Name _____   Date _____

1. Solve using number bonds with pairs of number sentences. You may draw quick tens and some ones to help you.

a. 19 + 12 = _____	b. 18 + 12 = _____
c. 19 + 13 = _____	d. 18 + 14 = _____
e. 17 + 14 = _____	f. 17 + 17 = _____
g. 18 + 17 = _____	h. 18 + 19 = _____

EUREKA
MATH

Lesson 27: Add a pair of two-digit numbers when the ones digits have a sum greater than 10.

© 2018 Great Minds®. eureka-math.org

165

2. Solve. You may draw quick tens and some ones to help you.

a. 19 + 12 = _____	b. 18 + 13 = _____
c. 19 + 13 = _____	d. 18 + 15 = _____
e. 19 + 16 = _____	f. 15 + 17 = _____
g. 19 + 19 = _____	h. 18 + 18 = _____

Lesson 27:   Add a pair of two-digit numbers when the ones digits have a sum
               greater than 10.

Name _____   Date _____

Solve using number bonds with pairs of number sentences. You may draw quick tens and some ones to help you.

a. 16 + 15 = _____	b. 17 + 13 = _____
c. 16 + 16 = _____	d. 17 + 15 = _____

EUREKA MATH

Lesson 27:   Add a pair of two-digit numbers when the ones digits have a sum greater than 10.

167

© 2018 Great Minds®. eureka-math.org

Read

Anton had some crayons in his desk. His teacher gave him 2 more. When he counted all of his crayons, he had 16 crayons. How many crayons did Anton have in his desk originally?

Draw

EUREKA
MATH

Lesson 28:   Add a pair of two-digit numbers with varied sums in the ones.

© 2018 Great Minds®. eureka-math.org

169

Write

_____

_____

_____

Lesson 28:   Add a pair of two-digit numbers with varied sums in the ones.

EUREKA MATH

Name _____   Date _____

1. Solve using quick ten drawings, number bonds, or the arrow way. Check the rectangle if you made a new ten.

a. 23 + 12 = _____	b. 15 + 15 = _____
c. 19 + 21 = _____	d. 17 + 12 = _____
e. 27 + 13 = _____	f. 17 + 16 = _____

Lesson 28:   Add a pair of two-digit numbers with varied sums in the ones.

© 2018 Great Minds®. eureka-math.org

171

2. Solve using quick ten drawings, number bonds, or the arrow way.

a. 15 + 13 = _____	b. 25 + 13 = _____
c. 24 + 14 = _____	d. 25 + 15 = _____
e. 18 + 14 = _____	f. 18 + 18 = _____
g. 24 + 16 = _____	h. 17 + 18 = _____

Lesson 28:   Add a pair of two-digit numbers with varied sums in the ones.

© 2018 Great Minds®. eureka-math.org

EUREKA
MATH®

Name _____   Date _____

Solve using quick tens and ones, number bonds, or the arrow way.

a. 12 + 16 = _____	b. 26 + 14 = _____
c. 18 + 16 = _____	d. 19 + 17 = _____

Read

Kiana's friend gave her 3 more stickers. Now, Kiana has 16 stickers. How many stickers did Kiana already have?

Draw

Write

_____

_____

_____

Name _____   Date _____

1. Solve using quick ten drawings, number bonds, or the arrow way.

a. 13 + 12 = _____	b. 23 + 12 = _____
c. 13 + 16 = _____	d. 23 + 16 = _____
e. 13 + 27 = _____	f. 17 + 16 = _____
g. 14 + 18 = _____	h. 18 + 17 = _____

2. Solve using quick ten drawings, number bonds, or the arrow way. Be prepared to discuss how you solved during the Debrief.

a. 17 + 11 = _____	b. 17 + 21 = _____
c. 27 + 13 = _____	d. 17 + 14 = _____
e. 13 + 26 = _____	f. 17 + 17 = _____
g. 18 + 15 = _____	h. 16 + 17 = _____

EUREKA MATH

Name _____   Date _____

Solve using quick ten drawings, number bonds, or the arrow way.

a. 18 + 14 = _____	b. 14 + 23 = _____
c. 28 + 12 = _____	d. 19 + 21 = _____

Lesson 29:   Add a pair of two-digit numbers with varied sums in the ones.

© 2018 Great Minds®. eureka-math.org

179

Grade 1
Module 5

Read

Today, everyone will get 7 straw pieces to use in our lesson. Later, you will use your pieces and your partner's pieces together. How many straw pieces will you have to use when you and your partner put them together?

Draw

Write

_____

_____

_____

Name _____   Date _____

1. Circle the shapes that have 5 straight sides.

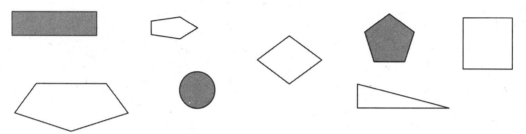

2. Circle the shapes that have no straight sides.

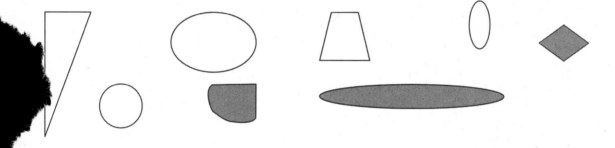

3. Circle the shapes where every corner is a square corner.

4.

a. Draw a shape that has 3 straight sides.	b. Draw another shape with 3 straight sides that is different from 4(a) and from the ones above.

EUREKA MATH

Lesson 1:   Classify shapes based on defining attributes using examples, variants, and non-examples.

185

© 2018 Great Minds®. eureka-math.org

5. Which attributes, or characteristics, are the same for all of the shapes in Group A?

GROUP A

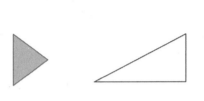  

They all _____ .

They all _____ .

6. Circle the shape that best fits with Group A.

7. Draw 2 more shapes that would fit in Group A.	8. Draw 1 shape that would **not** fit in Group A.

Lesson 1:   Classify shapes based on defining attributes using examples, variants, and non-examples.

Name _____   Date _____

1. How many corners and straight sides does each of the shapes below have?

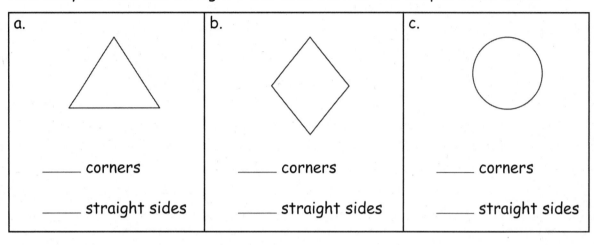

a.

_____ corners

_____ straight sides

b.

_____ corners

_____ straight sides

c.

_____ corners

_____ straight sides

2. Look at the sides and corners of the shapes in each row.

a. Cross off the shape that does not have the same number of sides and corners.

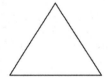 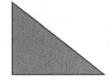 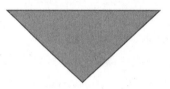

b. Cross off the shape that does not have the same kind of corners as the other shapes.

  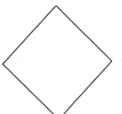

EUREKA MATH®

Lesson 1:   Classify shapes based on defining attributes using examples, variants, and non-examples.

© 2018 Great Minds®. eureka-math.org

187

Read

Lee has 9 straws. He uses 4 straws to make a shape. How many straws does he have left to make other shapes?

Extension: What possible shapes could Lee have created? Draw the different shapes Lee might have made using 4 straws. Label any shapes whose name you know.

Draw

Write

_____

_____

_____

Find and name two-dimensional shapes including trapezoid, rhombus, and a square as a special rectangle, based on defining attributes of sides and corners.

EUREKA MATH

Name _____   Date _____

1. Use the key to color the shapes. Write how many of each shape are in the picture.
    Whisper the name of the shape as you work.

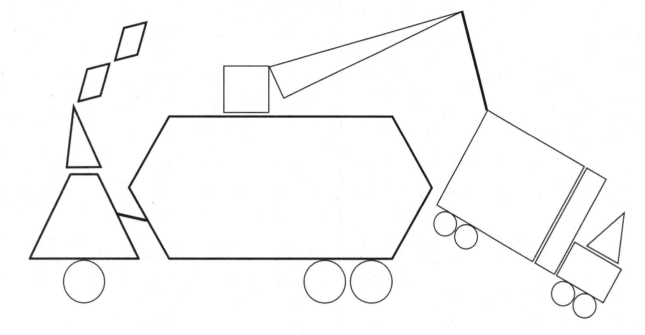

a. RED—4-sided shapes: _____   b. GREEN—3-sided shapes: _____

c. YELLOW—5-sided shapes: _____   d. BLACK—6-sided shapes: _____

e. BLUE—shapes with no corners: _____

EUREKA MATH®

Lesson 2:   Find and name two-dimensional shapes including trapezoid, rhombus,
and a square as a special rectangle, based on defining attributes of
sides and corners.
© 2018 Great Minds®. eureka-math.org

191

2. Circle the shapes that are rectangles.

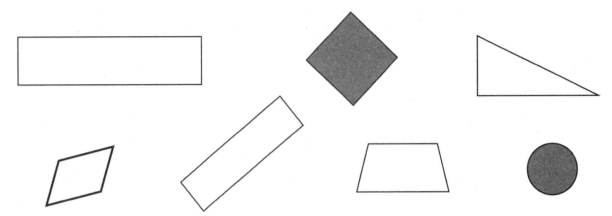

3. Is the shape a rectangle? Explain your thinking.

a.

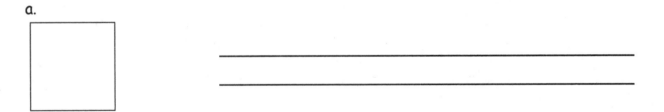

b.

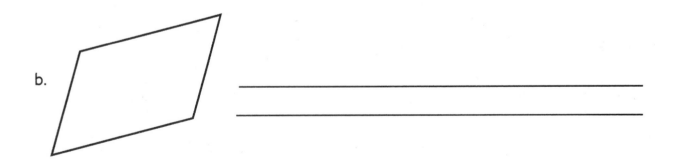

Lesson 2:   Find and name two-dimensional shapes including trapezoid, rhombus,
and a square as a special rectangle, based on defining attributes of
sides and corners.
© 2018 Great Minds®. eureka-math.org

EUREKA
MATH®

Name _____   Date _____

Write the number of corners and sides that each shape has. Then, match the shape to its name. Remember that some special shapes may have more than one name.

1.

_____ corners

_____ straight sides

triangle

circle

2.

_____ corners

_____ straight sides

rectangle

3.

_____ corners

_____ straight sides

hexagon

square

4.

_____ corners

_____ straight sides

rhombus

Lesson 2:   Find and name two-dimensional shapes including trapezoid, rhombus, and a square as a special rectangle, based on defining attributes of sides and corners.

© 2018 Great Minds®. eureka-math.org

193

Read

Rose draws 6 triangles. Maria draws 7 triangles. How many more triangles does Maria have than Rose?

Draw

Write

_____

_____

_____

Lesson 3:   Find and name three-dimensional shapes including cone and rectangular prism, based on defining attributes of faces and points.

195

© 2018 Great Minds®. eureka-math.org

Name _____ Date _____

1. On the first 4 objects, color one of the flat faces red. Match each 3-dimensional shape to its name.

a.

●

Rectangular prism

b.

●

Cone

c.

●

Sphere

d.

●

Cylinder

e.

●

Cube

 Lesson 3: Find and name three-dimensional shapes including cone and rectangular prism, based on defining attributes of faces and points.

197

© 2018 Great Minds®. eureka-math.org

2. Write the name of each object in the correct column.

block

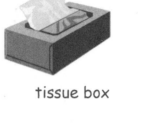

dice

can

tissue box

globe   tennis ball   party hat

Cubes	Spheres	Cones	Rectangular Prisms	Cylinders

3. Circle the attributes that describe ALL spheres.

are round

have no straight sides

can bounce

can roll

4. Circle the attributes that describe ALL cubes.

are red

have square faces

are hard   have 6 faces

Name _____   Date _____

Circle true or false. Write one sentence to explain your answer. Use the word bank if needed.

Word Bank

faces	circle	square
sides	rectangle	point

1.

This can is a cylinder.	True or False

2.

This juice box is a cube.	True or False

Lesson 3:   Find and name three-dimensional shapes including cone and rectangular prism, based on defining attributes of faces and points.

199

© 2018 Great Minds®. eureka-math.org

Read

Anton made a tower 5 cubes high. Ben made a tower 7 cubes high. How much taller is Ben's tower than Anton's?

Draw

Write

_____

_____

_____

Name _____   Date _____

Use pattern blocks to create the following shapes. Trace or draw to record your work.

1. Use 3 triangles to make 1 trapezoid.	2. Use 4 squares to make 1 larger square.
3. Use 6 triangles to make 1 hexagon.	4. Use 1 trapezoid, 1 rhombus, and 1 triangle to make 1 hexagon.

5. Make a rectangle using the Squares from the pattern blocks. Trace the Squares to show the rectangle you made.

6. How many squares do you see in this rectangle?

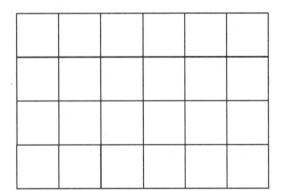

I can find _____ squares in this rectangle.

7. Use your pattern blocks to make a picture. Trace the shapes to show what you made. Tell a partner what shapes you used. Can you find any larger shapes within your picture?

Lesson 4:   Create composite shapes from two-dimensional shapes.   **EUREKA MATH**

Name _____   Date _____

Use pattern blocks to create the following shapes. Trace or draw to show what you did.

1. Use 3 rhombuses to make a hexagon.	2. Use 1 hexagon and 3 triangles to make a large triangle.

Read

Darnell and Tamra are comparing their grapes. Darnell's vine has 9 grapes.

Tamra's vine has 6 grapes. How many more grapes does Darnell have

than Tamra?

Draw

Write

_____

_____

_____

Name _____   Date _____

1.

   a. How many shapes were used to make this large square?

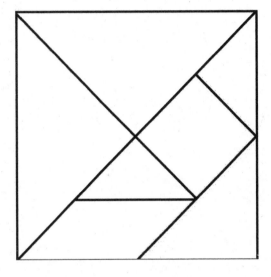

                              There are _____
                              shapes in this large square.

   b. What are the names of the 3 types of shapes used to make the large square?

_____   _____   _____

2. Use 2 of your tangram pieces to make a square. Which 2 pieces did you use? Draw or trace the pieces to show how you made the square.

3. Use 4 of your tangram pieces to make a trapezoid. Draw or trace the pieces to show the shapes you used.

4. Use all 7 tangram pieces to complete the puzzle.

5. With a partner, make a bird or a flower using all of your pieces. Draw or trace to show the pieces you used on the back of your paper. Experiment to see what other objects you can make with your pieces. Draw or trace to show what you created on the back of your paper.

EUREKA
MATH®

Name _____   Date _____

Use words or drawings to show how you can make a larger shape with 3 smaller shapes. Remember to use the names of the shapes in your example.

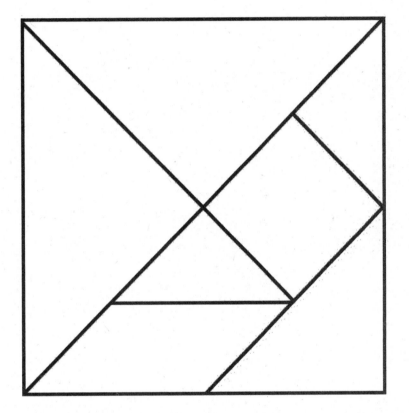

tangram

Read

Emi lined up 4 yellow cubes in a row. Fran lined up 7 blue cubes in a row.

Who has fewer cubes? How many fewer cubes does she have?

Draw

Write

_____

_____

_____

Lesson 6: Create a composite shape from three-dimensional shapes and describe the composite shape using shape names and positions.

© 2018 Great Minds®. eureka-math.org

215

Name _____ Date _____

1. Work with your partner and another pair to build a structure with your 3-dimensional shapes. You can use as many of the pieces as you choose.

2. Complete the chart to record the number of each shape you used to make your structure.

Cubes	
Spheres	
Rectangular Prisms	
Cylinders	
Cones	

3. Which shape did you use on the bottom of your structure? Why?

4. Is there a shape you chose not to use? Why or why not?

Lesson 6: Create a composite shape from three-dimensional shapes and describe the composite shape using shape names and positions.

217

© 2018 Great Minds®. eureka-math.org

Name _____   Date _____

Maria made a structure using her 3-dimensional shapes. Use your shapes to try to make the same structure as Maria as your teacher reads the description of Maria's structure.

Maria's structure has the following:

- 1 rectangular prism with the shortest face touching the table.
- 1 cube on top and to the right of the rectangular prism.
- 1 cylinder on top of the cube with the circular face touching the cube.

Lesson 6:   Create a composite shape from three-dimensional shapes and describe the composite shape using shape names and positions.

© 2018 Great Minds®. eureka-math.org

219

Read

Peter set up 5 rectangular prisms to make 5 towers. He put a cone on top of 3 of the towers. How many more cones does Peter need to have a cone on every tower?

Draw

Write

_____

_____

_____

 EUREKA MATH   Lesson 7:   Name and count shapes as parts of a whole, recognizing relative sizes
of the parts.

© 2018 Great Minds®. eureka-math.org

221

Name _____   Date _____

1. Are the shapes divided into equal parts? Write **Y** for yes or **N** for no. If the shape
    has equal parts, write how many equal parts on the line. The first one has been
    done for you.

a. **Y** ___ **2** ___	b. ___ ___	c. ___ ___
d. ___ ___	e. ___ ___	f. ___
g. ___ ___	h. ___ ___	i. ___ ___
j. ___ ___	k. ___ ___	l. ___ ___
m. ___ ___	n. ___ ___	o. ___ ___

EUREKA
MATH

Lesson 7:   Name and count shapes as parts of a whole, recognizing relative sizes
of the parts.

223

© 2018 Great Minds®. eureka-math.org

2. Write the number of equal parts in each shape.

a. _____	b. _____	c. _____
d. _____	e. _____	f. _____

3. Draw one line to make this triangle into 2 equal triangles.

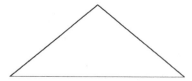

4. Draw one line to make this square into 2 equal parts.

5. Draw two lines to make this square into 4 equal squares.

Lesson 7:   Name and count shapes as parts of a whole, recognizing relative sizes
of the parts.

EUREKA
MATH

Name _____   Date _____

Circle the shape that has equal parts.

How many equal parts does the shape have? _____

EUREKA MATH

Lesson 7:   Name and count shapes as parts of a whole, recognizing relative sizes
             of the parts.

© 2018 Great Minds®. eureka-math.org

225

Read

Peter and Fran each have an equal number of pattern blocks. There are 12 pattern blocks altogether. How many pattern blocks does Fran have?

Draw

Write

_____

_____

_____

   Lesson 8:   Partition shapes and identify halves and quarters of circles and
rectangles.

© 2018 Great Minds®. eureka-math.org   227

Name _____   Date _____

1. Are the shapes divided into halves? Write yes or no.

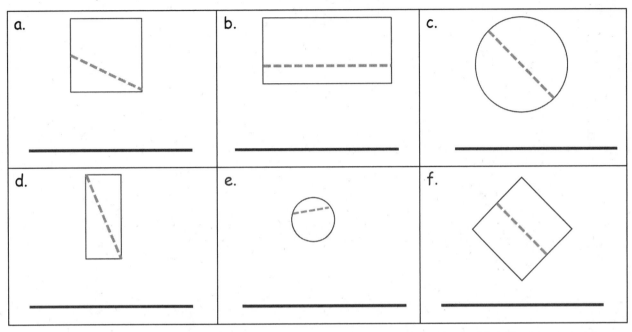

2. Are the shapes divided into quarters? Write yes or no.

3. Color half of each shape.

a.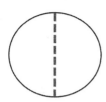

b.

c.

d.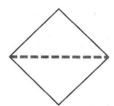

e.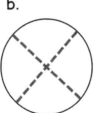

f.

4. Color 1 fourth of each shape.

a.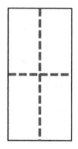

b.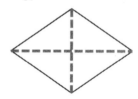

c.

d.

e.

    Lesson 8:   Partition shapes and identify halves and quarters of circles and rectangles.

EUREKA MATH®

Name _____   Date _____

Color 1 fourth of this square.	Color half of this rectangle.
Color half of this square.	Color a quarter of this circle.

Lesson 8: Partition shapes and identify halves and quarters of circles and rectangles.

© 2018 Great Minds®. eureka-math.org

231

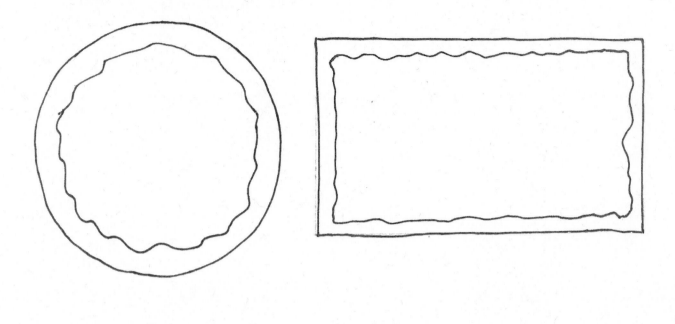

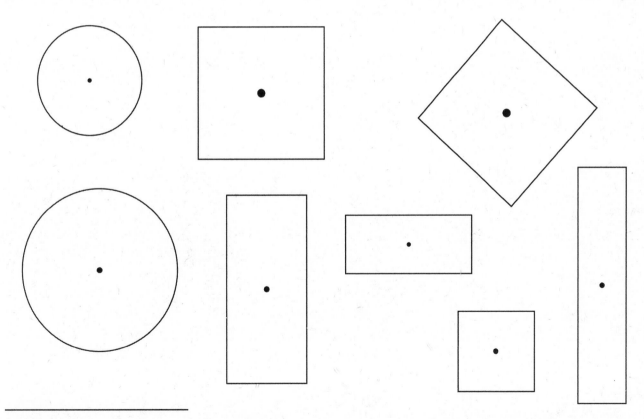

circles and rectangles

Lesson 8:   Partition shapes and identify halves and quarters of circles and
              rectangles.

© 2018 Great Minds®. eureka-math.org

233

Read

Emi cut a square brownie into fourths. Draw a picture of the brownie. Emi gave away 3 parts of the brownie. How many pieces does she have left?

Extension: What part, or fraction, of the whole brownie is left?

Draw

Lesson 9:   Partition shapes and identify halves and quarters of circles and rectangles.

© 2018 Great Minds®. eureka-math.org

235

Write

Lesson 9: Partition shapes and identify halves and quarters of circles and rectangles.

© 2018 Great Minds®. eureka-math.org

EUREKA MATH®

Name _____   Date _____

Label the shaded part of each picture as one half of the shape or one quarter of the shape.

1.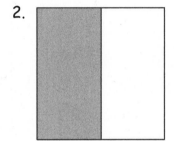

A   B

Which shape has been cut into more equal parts? _____

Which shape has larger equal parts? _____

Which shape has smaller equal parts? _____

2.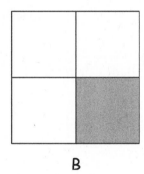

A   B

Which shape has been cut into more equal parts? _____

Which shape has larger equal parts? _____

Which shape has smaller equal parts? _____

3. Circle the shape that has a larger shaded part. Circle the phrase that makes the sentence true.

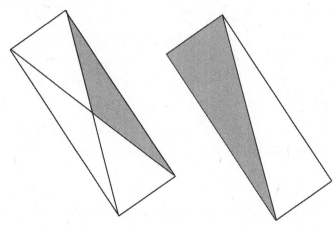

The larger shaded part is

(one half of / one quarter of)

the whole shape.

EUREKA MATH

Lesson 9:   Partition shapes and identify halves and quarters of circles and rectangles.

© 2018 Great Minds®. eureka-math.org

237

Color part of the shape to match its label.

Circle the phrase that would make the statement true.

4.

one half of the circle.

is larger than

is smaller than

is the same size as

one fourth of the circle.

5.

One quarter of the rectangle

is larger than

is smaller than

is the same size as

one half of the rectangle.

6.

One quarter of the square

is larger than

is smaller than

is the same size as

one fourth of the square.

Lesson 9:   Partition shapes and identify halves and quarters of circles and rectangles.

EUREKA
MATH®

Name _____   Date _____

1. Circle **T** for true or **F** for false.

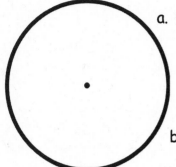

     a. One fourth of the circle is larger than one half of the circle.

                                                                    T   F

     b. Cutting the circle into quarters gives you more pieces than cutting the circle into halves.   **T   F**

2. Explain your answers using the circles below.

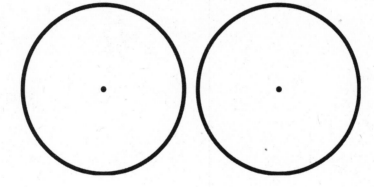

_____

_____

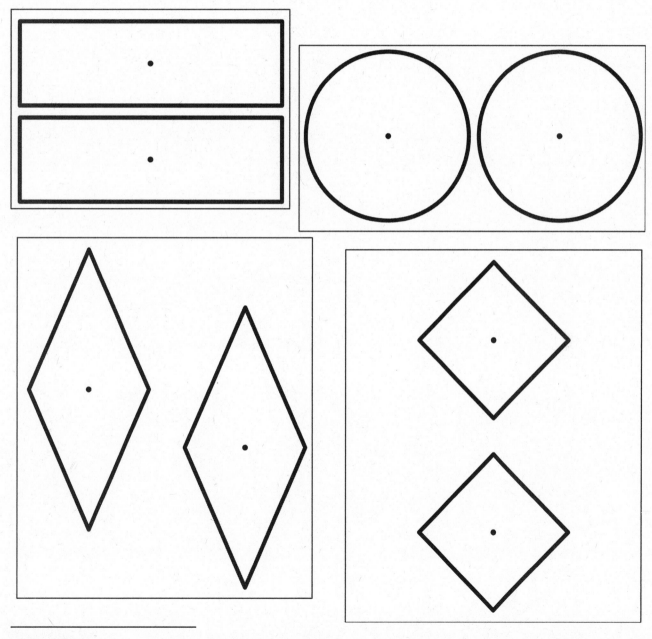

pairs of shapes

Lesson 9: Partition shapes and identify halves and quarters of circles and rectangles.

241

© 2018 Great Minds®. eureka-math.org

Read

Kim drew 7 circles. Shanika drew 10 circles. How many fewer circles did Kim draw than Shanika?

Draw

Write

_____

_____

_____

Name _____   Date _____

1. Match the clocks that show the same time.

a.   b.   c.   d.

●   ●   ●   ●

●   ●   ●   ●

2. Put the hour hand on this clock so that the clock reads 3 o'clock.

EUREKA MATH

Lesson 10: Construct a paper clock by partitioning a circle and tell time to the hour.

© 2018 Great Minds®. eureka-math.org

245

3. Write the time shown on each clock.

a. _____ : _____

b. _____ o'clock

c. _____ o'clock

d. _____ o'clock

e. _____ : _____

f. _____ o'clock

g. _____ : _____

h. _____ o'clock

i. _____ : _____

j. _____ o'clock

k. _____ : _____

l. _____ o'clock

m. _____

n. _____

o. _____

Lesson 10: Construct a paper clock by partitioning a circle and tell time to the hour.

EUREKA MATH

Name _____   Date _____

Write the time shown on each clock.

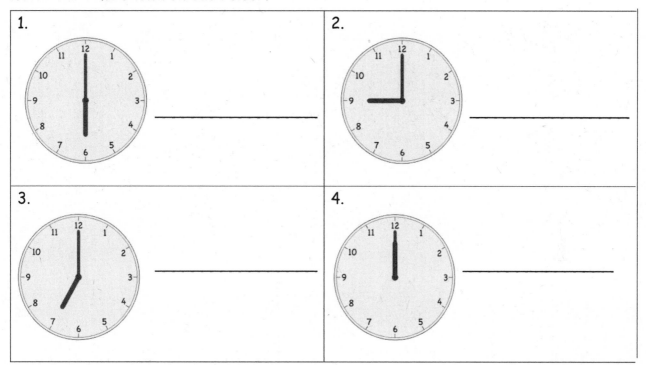

1. _____

2. _____

3. _____

4. _____

EUREKA
MATH

Lesson 10:   Construct a paper clock by partitioning a circle and tell time to the
                 hour.

247

© 2018 Great Minds®. eureka-math.org

Read

Tamra has 7 digital clocks in her house and only 2 circular or analog clocks. How many fewer circular clocks does Tamra have than digital clocks? How many clocks does Tamra have altogether?

Draw

Write

_____

_____

_____

Lesson 11:   Recognize halves within a circular clock face and tell time to the half hour.

249

Name _____   Date _____

1. Match the clocks to the times on the right.

a.

b.

c.

● Half past 5 o'clock

● **12:30**

● **2:30**

● Five thirty

● Half past 12 o'clock

● Two thirty

2. Draw the minute hand so the clock shows the time written above it.

a. 7 o'clock   b. 8 o'clock   c. 7:30

d. 1:30   e. 2:30   f. 2 o'clock

3. Write the time shown on each clock. Complete problems like the first two examples.

a.

b. **5:30**

3:30   five thirty

c. _____

d. **12:30**

e. _____

f. _____

g. _____

h. _____

i. _____

j. **7:30**

k. _____

l. **10:30**

4. Circle the clock that shows half past 12 o'clock.

a.   b.   c.

Lesson 11:   Recognize halves within a circular clock face and tell time to the half
                                    hour.

EUREKA
MATH®

Name _____   Date _____

Draw the minute hand so the clock shows the time written above it.

1.
9:30

2.
3:30

3. Write the correct time on the line.

   _____

Read

Shade the clock from the start of a new hour through half an hour.

Explain why that is the same as 30 minutes.

Draw

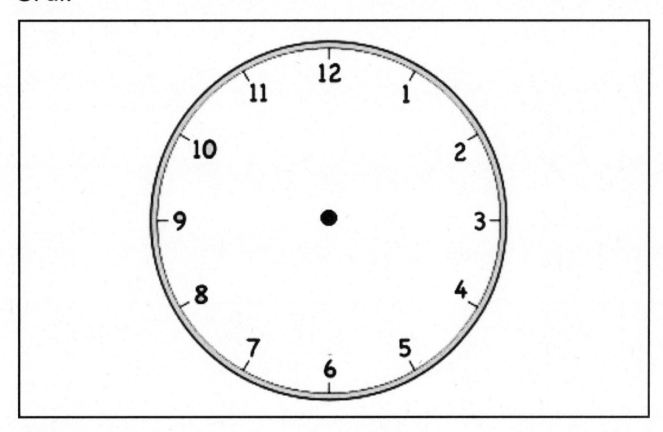

Write

_____

_____

_____

Name _____   Date _____

Fill in the blanks.

1.

A   B

Clock _____ shows half past eleven.

2.

A   B

Clock _____ shows half past two.

3.

A   B

Clock _____ shows 6 o'clock.

4.

A   B

Clock _____ shows 9:30.

5.

A   B

Clock _____ shows half past six.

Lesson 12:   Recognize halves within a circular clock face and tell time to the half
             hour.

© 2018 Great Minds®. eureka-math.org

257

6. Match the clocks.

a.

b.

c.

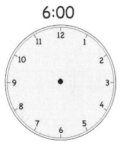

d.

half past 7

half past 1

7 o'clock

half past 5

7. Draw the minute and hour hands on the clocks.

a.   3:30

b.   8:30

c.   11:00

d.   6:00

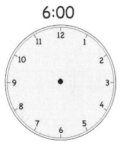

e.   4:30

f.   12:30

Lesson 12:   Recognize halves within a circular clock face and tell time to the half hour.

Name _____ Date _____

Draw the minute and hour hands on the clocks.

1.   1:30

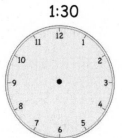

2.   10:00

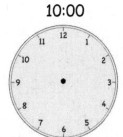

3.   5:30

4.   7:30

EUREKA
MATH®

Lesson 12:   Recognize halves within a circular clock face and tell time to the half
                      hour.

259

© 2018 Great Minds®. eureka-math.org

Read

Ben is a clock collector. He has 8 digital clocks and 5 circular clocks. How many clocks does Ben have altogether? How many more digital clocks does Ben have than circular clocks?

Draw

Write

_____

_____

_____

Lesson 13:   Recognize halves within a circular clock face and tell time to the half hour.

261

© 2018 Great Minds®. eureka-math.org

Name _Tulsi,1.9_____ Date _4/4/2024_

Circle the correct clock. Write the times for the other two clocks on the lines.

1. Circle the clock that shows half past 1 o'clock.

a.    b.    c.

_a.100_
_c.12:30_

2. Circle the clock that shows 7 o'clock.

a.    b. 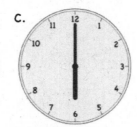   c.

_b.8.00_
_c.12:30_

3. Circle the clock that shows half past 10 o'clock.

a.    b.    c.

_a.1130_
_b.11.00_

4. What time is it? Write the times on the lines.

a. 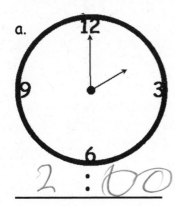   b.    c.

_2 : 00_   _4 : 30_   _10:00_

EUREKA
MATH®

Lesson 13: Recognize halves within a circular clock face and tell time to the half hour.

263

© 2018 Great Minds®. eureka-math.org

5. Draw the **minute** and **hour** hands on the clocks.

a.   1:00

b.   1:30

c.   2:00

d.   6:30

e.   7:30

f.   8:30

g.   10:00

h.   11:00

i.   12:00

j.   9:30

k.   3:00

l.   5:30

Lesson 13:   Recognize halves within a circular clock face and tell time to the half hour.

EUREKA MATH®

Name _____   Date _____

1. Circle the clock(s) that shows half past 3 o'clock.

a.    b.    c.

2. Write the time or draw the hands on the clocks.

a. 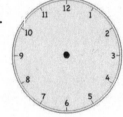   b.    c.

4:30   _____   9 o'clock

EUREKA MATH

Lesson 13:   Recognize halves within a circular clock face and tell time to the half hour.

© 2018 Great Minds®. eureka-math.org

265

clock images

Lesson 13:   Recognize halves within a circular clock face and tell time to the half hour.

267

Credits

Great Minds® has made every effort to obtain permission for the reprinting of all copyrighted material. If any owner of copyrighted material is not acknowledged herein, please contact Great Minds for proper acknowledgment in all future editions and reprints of this module.